Collins

Step Up Workbook 3

Maggie Green

Name ....

Class: ....

NEW MATHS FRAMEWORKING

Jeanette Mumford
Simon and Helen Greaves

Contents

NUMBER AND ALGEBRA

1.1 Place value in numbers

- I can read and write numbers up to and over 1000.

Key words
digit, thousands, hundreds, tens, units

Numbers from 100 to 999 have three digits. The first digit tells you the number of hundreds. The second digit tells you the number of tens. The third digit tells you the number of units.

250

Two hundred and fifty has
2 hundreds, 5 tens and 0 units.

908

Nine hundred and eight has
9 hundreds, 0 tens and 8 units.

In a four-digit number the first digit tells you the number of thousands.

1257

One thousand, two hundred and fifty-seven has 1 thousand, 2 hundreds, 5 tens and 7 units.

2500

Two thousand, five hundred has 2 thousands, 5 hundreds, 0 tens and 0 units.

1 Write each number in figures.

a Three hundred and twenty-two
322

b Two hundred and eighty-seven
287

c Four hundred and eighteen
418

d One thousand, five hundred and eighty-one
1,581

e Three thousand, four hundred
3,400

f Three hundred and six
306

g Nine hundred and forty
940

h Two thousand, eight hundred and nine
2,809

2 Write each number in words.

a 367 | Three hundred and sixty-seven

b 625 | Six hundred and Twenty five

c 882 | eight Hundred and eight Two

d 1974 | one Thowsand ~~nine~~ Hundred and Seventy for

e 670 | Six Hundred and Seventy

f 2219 | two thowsand Two Hundred and ninetern

g 408 | For hundred and eight

h 3920 |

3 Each sweatshirt has a number label.

a How many hundreds in the number on the red sweatshirt? **3** hundreds

b How many thousands in the number on the blue sweatshirt? **1** thousands

c How many units in the number on the brown sweatshirt? **3** units

d How many hundreds in the number on the white sweatshirt? **8** hundreds

◆ I can read and write numbers up to and over 1000. ✓

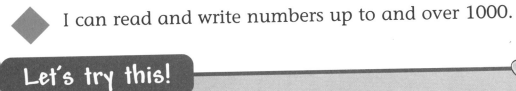

Let's try this!

Roll the dice four times. Write down the number each time to make a four-digit number. Write this number in words.

1.2 Ordering numbers

Key words
higher, lower, order, smaller, larger

Here are two three-digit numbers.

537   584

The number with the higher tens digit is the larger number.
584 is the larger number.
Here are two four-digit numbers.

1852   1753

The thousands digit is the same for both numbers so look at the hundreds digits. The number with the higher hundreds digit is the larger number. 1852 is the larger number.

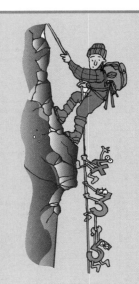

1 Circle the higher of the two numbers.

a

(437)   258

b

896   749

c

529   585

d

290   209

e

1800   1700

f

1609   1790

g

3457   3475

h

2380   2388

2 For each set of numbers, write the lowest number.

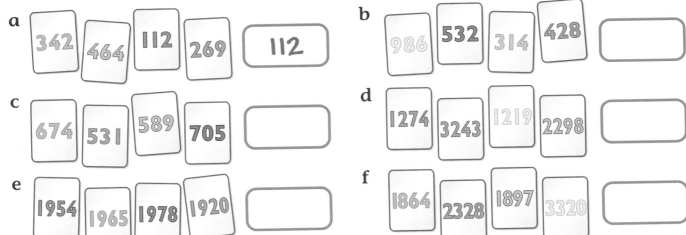

a
342 464 112 269 **112**

b
986 532 314 428 [ ]

c
674 531 589 705 [ ]

d
1274 3243 1219 2298 [ ]

e
1954 1965 1978 1920 [ ]

f
1864 2328 1897 3320 [ ]

3 Write these numbers in order from lowest to highest.

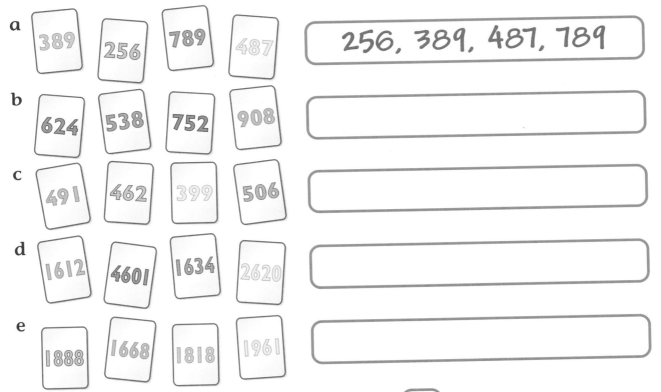

a
389 256 789 487 **256, 389, 487, 789**

b
624 538 752 908 [ ]

c
491 462 399 506 [ ]

d
1612 4601 1634 2620 [ ]

e
1888 1668 1818 1961 [ ]

◆ I can order numbers up to and over 1000. [ ]

Let's try this!

Use the digits 7, 2, 9 and 5 to make as many different four-digit numbers as you can. Write your numbers in order starting with the smallest.

7 2 9 5

Rounding numbers to the nearest 10 and 100

● I can round numbers to the nearest 10 and 100.

Here is a number line between 30 and 40.

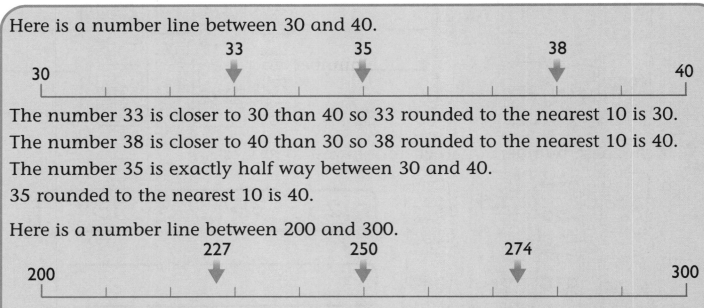

The number 33 is closer to 30 than 40 so 33 rounded to the nearest 10 is 30.
The number 38 is closer to 40 than 30 so 38 rounded to the nearest 10 is 40.
The number 35 is exactly half way between 30 and 40.
35 rounded to the nearest 10 is 40.

Here is a number line between 200 and 300.

The number 227 is closer to 200 than 300 so 227 rounded to the nearest 100 is 200.
The number 274 is closer to 300 than 200 so 274 rounded to the nearest 100 is 300.
The number 250 is exactly half way between 200 and 300.
250 rounded to the nearest 100 is 300.

1 Use the number lines to round these numbers to the nearest 10.

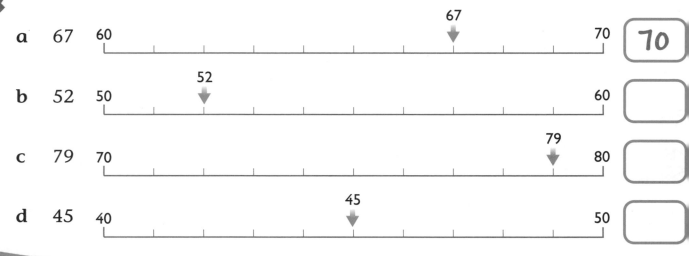

a   67   60 ———— 67 ———— 70   **70**

b   52   50 — 52 ———— 60   [ ]

c   79   70 ———— 79 — 80   [ ]

d   45   40 ———— 45 ———— 50   [ ]

2 Round each number to the nearest 10. Colour the correct box.

a   86   b   32   c   44   d   75

| 80 | 30 | 40 | 70 |

| 90 | 40 | 50 | 80 |

3 Use the number lines to round the numbers to the nearest hundred.

a   371   300 ──────────── 371 ──── 400   [ ]

b   620   600 ── 620 ──────────── 700   [ ]

c   589   500 ──────────── 589 ── 600   [ ]

d   450   400 ──────── 450 ──────── 500   [ ]

4 Round each number to the nearest 100. Colour the correct box.

a   262   b   189   c   758   d   350

| 200 | 100 | 700 | 300 |

| 300 | 200 | 800 | 400 |

◆ I can round numbers to the nearest 10 and 100.   [ ]

Let's try this!

Use a set of digit cards numbered 1 to 9. Choose three digit cards to make a three-digit number. Round your number to the nearest hundred.

463 rounded to nearest 100 is 500

1.4 Negative numbers

● I can count with negative numbers.

Key words
negative, sequence, count on, count back, zero

If you count back from zero the numbers become negative.
Counting back from zero in ones shows the sequence:

0, −1, −2, −3, −4, −5, −6, −7, ...

−5   −4   −3   −2   −1   0   1   2   3   4

1 Write in the missing numbers to complete each number line.

a   −4   **−3**   −2   **−1**   0   1   **2**   **3**   **4**   **5**

b   ☐   −5   ☐   −3   ☐   −1   0   ☐   2   3   ☐

c   ☐   −7   ☐   −5   ☐   ☐   −2   −1   0   1   ☐

d   ☐   ☐   ☐   ☐   0   ☐   2   ☐   ☐   5

2 Circle the smaller number for each pair of numbers.

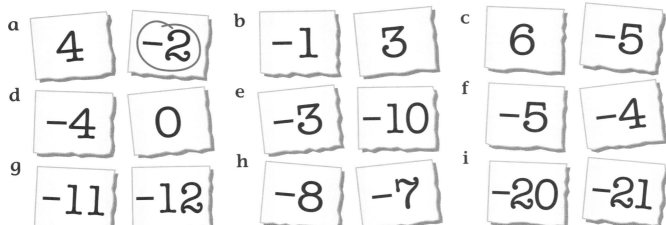

a   4   (−2)   b   −1   3   c   6   −5

d   −4   0   e   −3   −10   f   −5   −4

g   −11   −12   h   −8   −7   i   −20   −21

3 Complete each sequence by counting on or back in ones.

a   Count on   −5   −4   −3

b   Count back   3   2   1

c   Count on   −9   −8   −7

d   Count back   −2   −3   −4

e   Count on   −15   −14   −13

f   Count back   −8   −9   −10

◆   I can count with negative numbers. ☐

Let's try this!

Here are some negative numbers:

Choose one of the numbers. Roll a dice. Now count back from the number on the dice to the negative number you chose. Try this again.

- I can make sequences including those with negative numbers.

Key words
sequence, rule, negative, add, subtract

A **sequence** is a pattern of numbers.

The numbers in the sequence follow a **rule**.

The numbers in a sequence can be **negative**.

This sequence starts with the number 4. The rule is subtract 2.

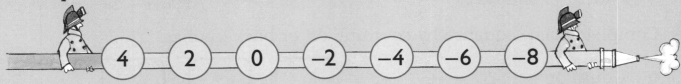

This sequence starts with the number –40. The rule is add 10.

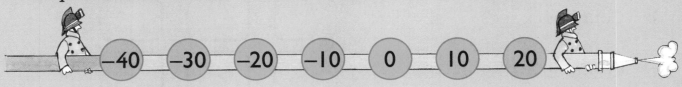

1 Use the rule to complete each sequence of numbers.

					–6	–4	–2	0
a	Add 2	–10	–8		–6	–4	–2	0
b	Add 10	–60	–50					
c	Add 5	–20	–15					
d	Subtract 2	5	3					
e	Subtract 10	10	0					
f	Subtract 5	0	–5					

2 Draw lines to join each sequence to the correct rule.

-30, -20, -10, 0, 10, 20   Add 5

-10, -5, 0, 5, 10, 15   Subtract 10

10, 5, 0, -5, -10, -15   Add 2

10, 0, -10, -20, -30, -40   Subtract 5

-12, -10, -8, -6, -4, -2   Add 10

3 Use the rule to complete the missing numbers in each sequence.

a	**+ 4**	-16	-12	-8	[ ]	0	4	[ ] [ ]
b	**+ 5**	-35	[ ]	-25	[ ] [ ]		-10	-5 [ ]
c	**+ 3**	-15	-12	[ ]	[ ]	-3	[ ]	3 [ ]
d	**- 5**	15	10	[ ]	[ ]	[ ]	-10	-15 [ ]
e	**- 4**	8	[ ]	[ ]	-4	[ ]	-12	[ ] -20

 I can make sequences including those with negative numbers. [ ]

Let's try this!

Here are some rules for sequences and some numbers.

Subtract 3

Subtract 4

Subtract 5

0

15

6

Choose one rule and one number. Start at the number you have chosen and use the rule to continue your sequence until you have six numbers in the sequence.
Try this for a different number and rule.

FRACTIONS AND DECIMALS
2.1 Fraction of a shape

● I can recognise fractions of shapes where more than one part is shaded.

Key words
fraction, numerator, denominator

Here is a shape divided into seven equal parts.

Three parts are shaded.

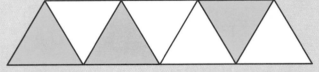

The fraction that is shaded is three sevenths. This is written as $\frac{3}{7}$.

The number at the bottom is called the **denominator**.

It tells you that the shape is divided into seven equal parts.

The number at the top is called the **numerator**.

It tells you that you have three parts.

1 Shade each shape to show these fractions.

a $\frac{2}{7}$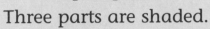

b $\frac{3}{8}$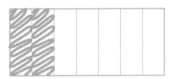

c $\frac{7}{9}$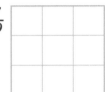

d $\frac{5}{6}$

e $\frac{3}{10}$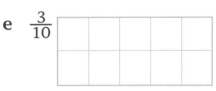

f $\frac{4}{7}$

2 Circle the correct fraction for each shape.

a $\frac{2}{9}$ $\frac{2}{7}$ $\frac{2}{8}$ $\frac{3}{7}$ b $\frac{5}{7}$ $\frac{5}{9}$ $\frac{5}{6}$ $\frac{4}{6}$ c $\frac{8}{10}$ $\frac{7}{9}$ $\frac{7}{10}$ $\frac{8}{9}$ d $\frac{5}{6}$ $\frac{4}{7}$ $\frac{5}{7}$ $\frac{5}{8}$

 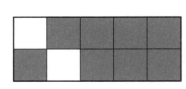 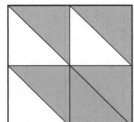

3 Write the fraction that is coloured blue in each shape.

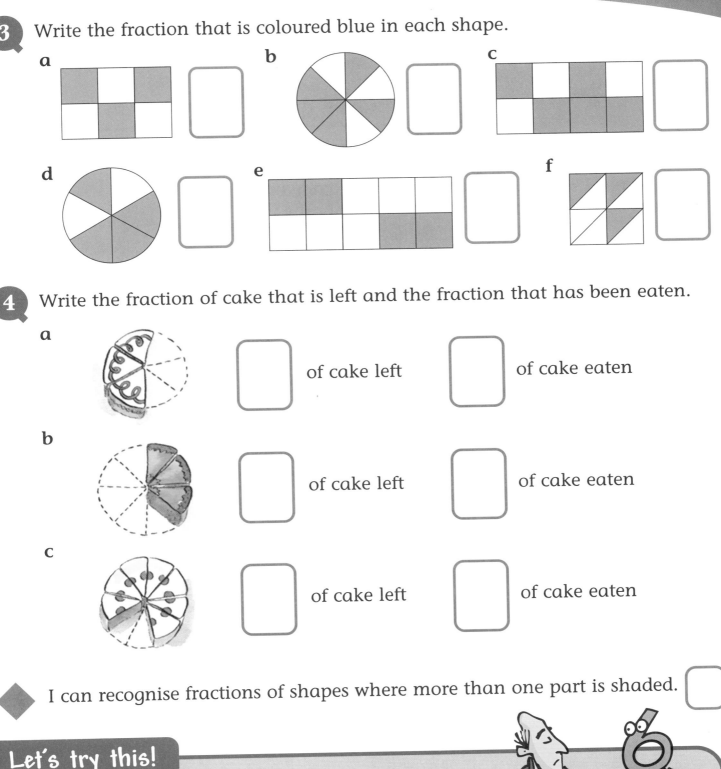

a

b

c

d

e

f

4 Write the fraction of cake that is left and the fraction that has been eaten.

a

of cake left   of cake eaten

b

of cake left   of cake eaten

c

of cake left   of cake eaten

I can recognise fractions of shapes where more than one part is shaded.

Let's try this!

Use the digit cards 2, 4, 6, 7, 8, 9 to make as many different fractions as possible.
The numerator (number at the top) must be smaller than the denominator (number at the bottom). Show these fractions as coloured shapes.

● I can recognise fractions that are equivalent.

Key words
halves, quarters, equivalent, fraction

This square is divided into two halves.

$\frac{1}{2}$ is coloured.

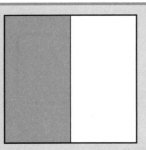

This square is divided into quarters.

$\frac{2}{4}$ are coloured.

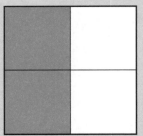

The same amount of each square is shaded so:

$\frac{1}{2} = \frac{2}{4}$

$\frac{1}{2}$ and $\frac{2}{4}$ are called **equivalent** fractions.

Here is another pair of equivalent fractions.

$\frac{1}{3} = \frac{2}{6}$

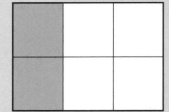

1 Put a tick below each shape that has $\frac{1}{2}$ coloured.

a
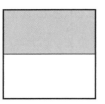

b
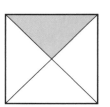

c

d
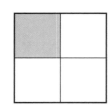

e

f
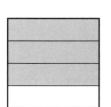

g
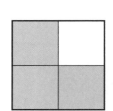

h
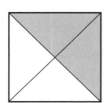

2 These shapes are divided into quarters. Shade $\frac{1}{2}$ (the same as $\frac{2}{4}$) of each shape in three different ways. The first one has been done for you.

a

b

c 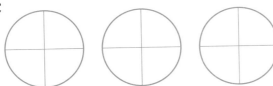   **d**

3 Write the pair of equivalent fractions for each shape.

a 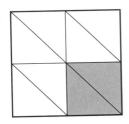   **b** 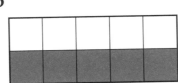   **c** 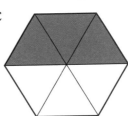   **d**

$\frac{2}{8} = \frac{1}{4}$    ▢

◆ I can recognise that fractions are equivalent. ▢

Let's try this!

Here is a strip of eight squares.

Use some squared paper and copy this strip four times. Find four different ways to shade $\frac{1}{2}$ of it. Now find four different ways to shade $\frac{1}{4}$.

2.3 Fraction of a number

- I can find a fraction of a set of objects.

Key words
fraction, equals, groups

Here are 12 balls.

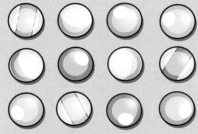

To find $\frac{2}{3}$ of the balls you need to share them into three equal groups.

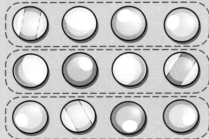

One group has four balls so $\frac{1}{3}$ of 12 is 4.
Two groups have eight balls so $\frac{2}{3}$ of 12 is 8.

Here are 10 balls.

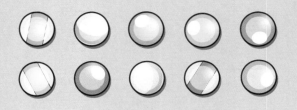

To find $\frac{3}{5}$ of the balls you need to share them into five equal groups.

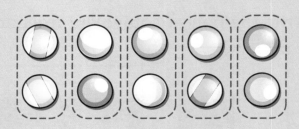

One group has two balls so $\frac{1}{5}$ of 10 is 2.
Three groups have six balls so $\frac{3}{5}$ of 10 is 6.

1 Complete the sentences about each tray.

a Here is a tray of eight buns.

There are four rows of two buns.

$\frac{1}{4}$ of 8 buns is ⟦ 2 ⟧ buns.

$\frac{2}{4}$ of 8 buns is ⟦ ⟧ buns.

$\frac{3}{4}$ of 8 buns is ⟦ ⟧ buns.

b Here is a tray of 16 buns.

There are four rows of four buns.

$\frac{1}{4}$ of 16 buns is ⟦ ⟧ buns.

$\frac{2}{4}$ of 16 buns is ⟦ ⟧ buns.

$\frac{3}{4}$ of 16 buns is ⟦ ⟧ buns.

2 Work out the fraction of each set of objects.

a

$\frac{1}{3}$ of 12 sweets is ⬜ **4** .

$\frac{2}{3}$ of 12 sweets is ⬜ .

b

$\frac{1}{3}$ of 18 ice-creams is ⬜ .

$\frac{2}{3}$ of 18 ice-creams is ⬜ .

c

$\frac{1}{4}$ of 28 cars is ⬜ .

$\frac{3}{4}$ of 28 cars is ⬜ .

d

$\frac{1}{6}$ of 30 pears is ⬜ .

$\frac{3}{6}$ of 30 pears is ⬜ .

e

$\frac{1}{5}$ of 35 oranges is ⬜ .

$\frac{2}{5}$ of 35 oranges is ⬜ .

f

$\frac{1}{4}$ of 20 pieces of chocolate is ⬜ .

$\frac{3}{4}$ of 20 pieces of chocolate is ⬜ .

◆ I can find a fraction of a set of objects. ⬜

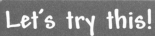

Let's try this!

Get 12 paper clips. Use them to find
different fractions of 12.
Find thirds, quarters and sixths of 12,
for example, $\frac{2}{3}$, $\frac{3}{4}$, $\frac{4}{6}$.

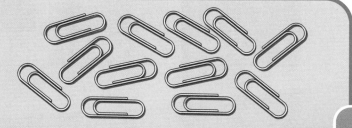

2.4 Mixed numbers

● I can write a fraction as a mixed number.

Key words
mixed number, whole number, fraction

A mixed number is a number that has a whole number and a fraction, for example, $1\frac{1}{2}$ or $2\frac{3}{4}$.

 　　　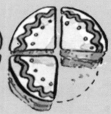

1 whole cake　　　$\frac{1}{2}$ cake = $1\frac{1}{2}$ cakes　　　1 whole cake　　1 whole cake　　$\frac{3}{4}$ cake = $2\frac{3}{4}$ cakes

1 Write the mixed number for each set of shapes.

a
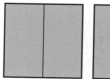 　$1\frac{1}{2}$

b

c

d

e
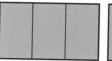 

f
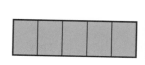 

g
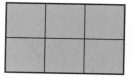 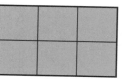 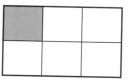

2 Colour the shapes to show the mixed number.

a $1\frac{1}{2}$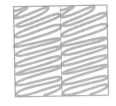

b $2\frac{1}{4}$

c $1\frac{1}{3}$

d $1\frac{2}{5}$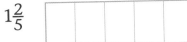

e $1\frac{5}{6}$

f $2\frac{3}{5}$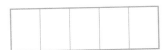

 I can write a fraction as a mixed number.

Let's try this!

Choose a mixed number. Make a drawing to show the mixed number. Repeat this for all the mixed numbers.

2.5 Tenths as decimals

- I can write tenths as fractions and decimals.

Key words
fraction, tenth, decimal

This rectangle is divided into 10 equal parts. Each part is one tenth.
This is written $\frac{1}{10}$ as a fraction and 0.1 as a decimal.

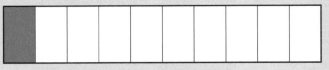

$$\frac{1}{10} = 0.1$$

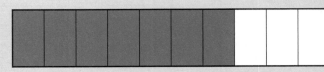

$$\frac{7}{10} = 0.7$$

$$1\frac{2}{10} = 1.2$$

1 Each shape is divided into tenths. Colour the decimal given.

a 0.6

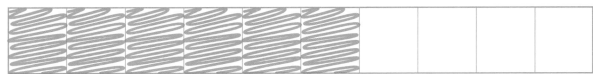

b 0.3

c 0.8

d 0.2

2 For each of these shapes, write the decimal that is coloured.

a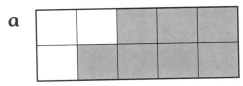

b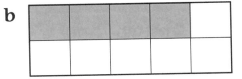

c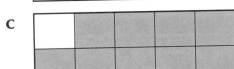

d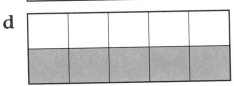

3 For each of these shapes, write the amount that is coloured as a decimal.

a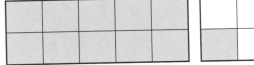

b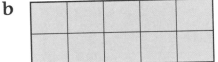

c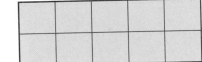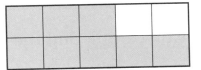

d

I can write tenths as fractions and decimals.

Let's try this!

Write each mixed number or fraction as a decimal.
Draw shapes to show each fraction or mixed number.

ADDITION AND SUBTRACTION

3.1 Adding two two-digit numbers

● I can add two two-digit numbers together using an empty number line.

Key words
add, digits, empty number line

Here is a way to add together two numbers with two digits each: 44 + 38

Split the second number
into tens and units: 44 + 30 + 8

Add the tens number
on first: 74 + 8

Now add on the units: 82

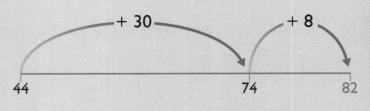

Here is another addition: 64 + 57

64 + 57 = 64 + 50 + 7

= 114 + 7 = 121

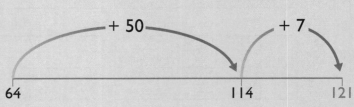

1 Add each pair of numbers by completing the empty number line.

a 36 + 55

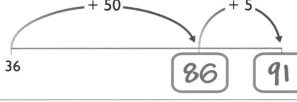

b 22 + 49

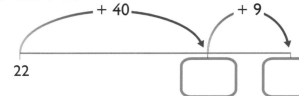

c 46 + 55

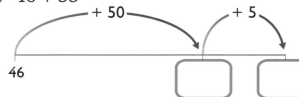

d 32 + 78

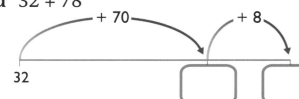

e 76 + 18

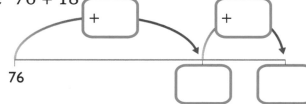

f 45 + 37

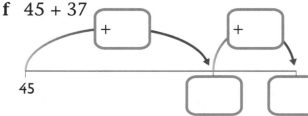

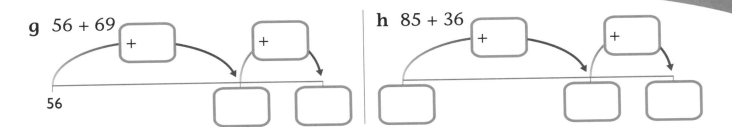

g 56 + 69

+   +

56

h 85 + 36

+   +

2 Add each pair of numbers. Use an empty number line to find the answer.

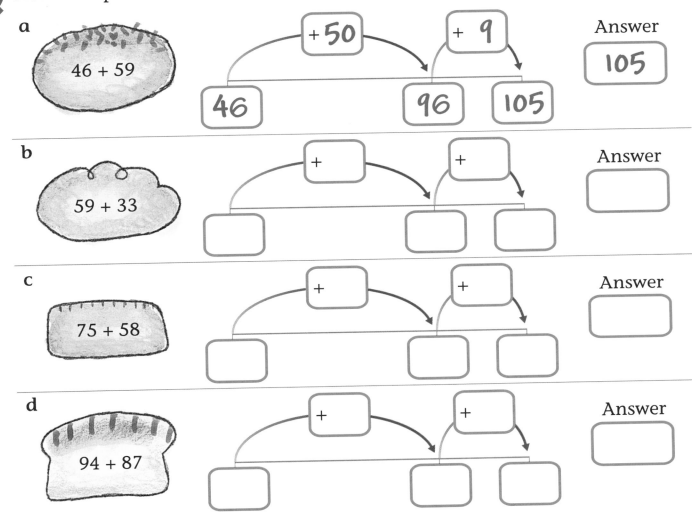

a

46 + 59

+50   + 9

46   96   105

Answer

105

b

59 + 33

+   +

Answer

c

75 + 58

+   +

Answer

d

94 + 87

+   +

Answer

◆ I can add two two-digit numbers together using an empty number line.

37 16 95 66
34 87 46 72

Adding a two-digit number to a three-digit number

- I can add a two-digit number to a three-digit number using an empty number line.

Key words
add, digits, empty number line

Here is a way to add a two-digit number to a three-digit number: 221 + 34

So 221 + 34 = 221 + 30 + 4 = 255

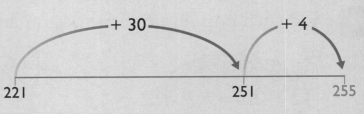

Here is another addition: 45 + 178

Start with the larger number, 178. Then add on 45.

So 178 + 45 = 178 + 40 + 5 = 223

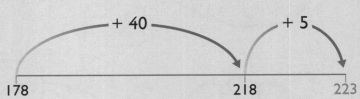

1 Add each pair of numbers by completing the empty number line.

a 126 + 68

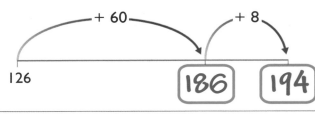

b 215 + 46

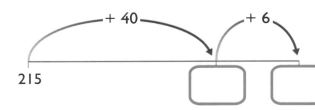

c 189 + 17

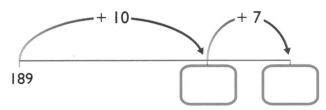

d 283 + 28

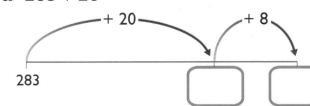

e 164 + 29

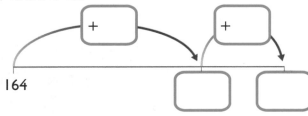

f 325 + 27

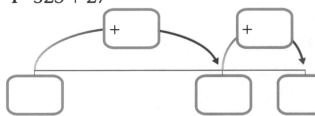

g 45 + 176

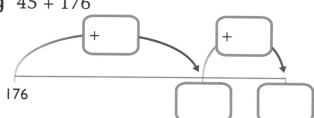

h 88 + 233

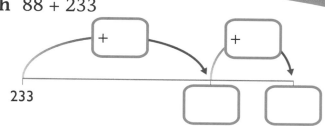

2 Add each pair of numbers. Use an empty number line to find the answer.

a

168 + 75

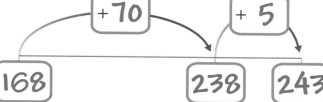

Answer

243

b

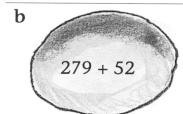

279 + 52

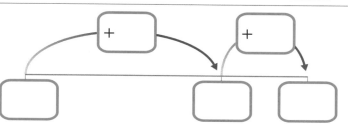

Answer

c

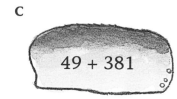

49 + 381

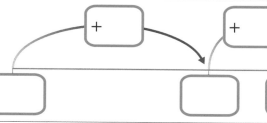

Answer

d

93 + 512

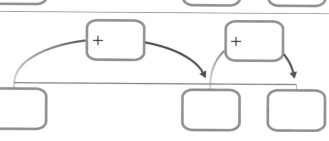

Answer

I can add a two-digit number to a three-digit number using an empty number line.

Let's try this!

Choose a two-digit and three-digit number. Add them together.
Repeat this for a different pair of numbers. Which pairs of numbers add up to give a total of more than 300?

3.3 Adding two three-digit numbers

- I can add two three-digit numbers together using an empty number line.

Key words
add, digits, empty number line

Here is a way to add one three-digit number to another three-digit number using an empty number line.

248 + 126

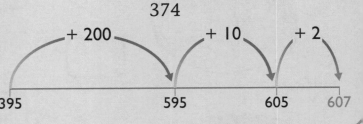

Split the second number into hundreds, tens and units

Add the hundreds number on first

Now add on the tens and then the units

248 + 100 + 20 + 6

348 + 20 + 6

368 + 6

374

Here is another example.

395 + 212

so 395 + 212 = 395 + 200 + 10 + 2 = 607

1 Add each pair of numbers by completing the empty number line.

a 132 + 164

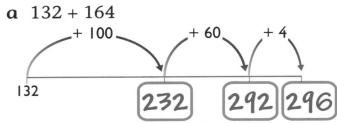

b 246 + 136

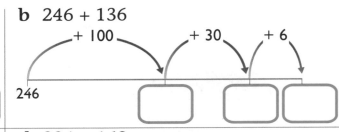

c 164 + 147

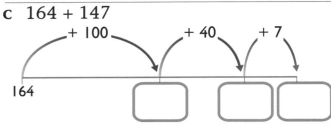

d 234 + 168

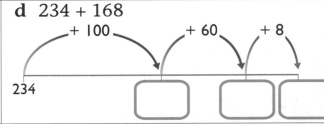

e 329 + 247

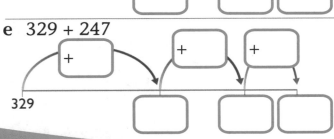

f 413 + 186

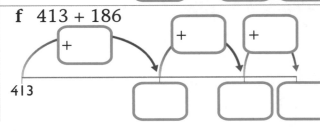

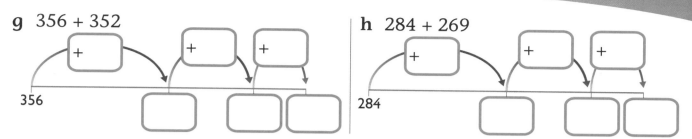

g 356 + 352

356

h 284 + 269

284

2 Add each pair of numbers. Use an empty number line to find the answer.

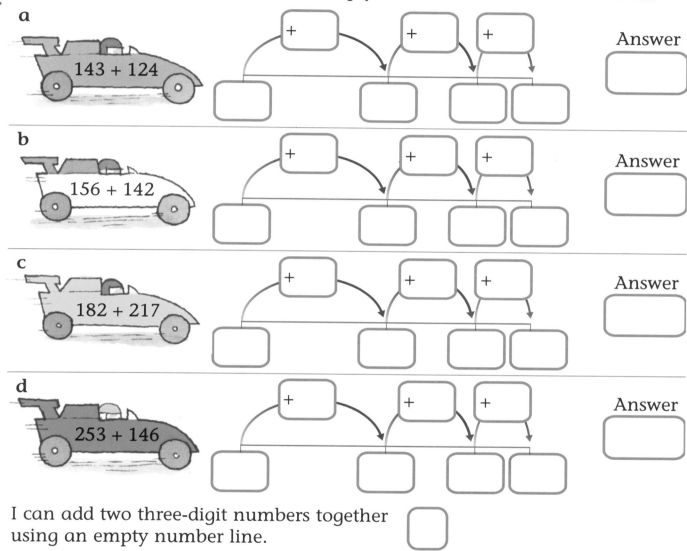

a

143 + 124

Answer

b

156 + 142

Answer

c

182 + 217

Answer

d

253 + 146

Answer

I can add two three-digit numbers together using an empty number line.

Let's try this!

Choose numbers on two footballs and add the numbers together. Repeat this for a different pair of footballs. Which pairs of footballs add up to less than 500?

101   489   268   245   341

Subtracting two two-digit numbers

- I can subtract a two-digit number from another two-digit number using an empty number line.

Here is a way to subtract a two-digit number from another two-digit number:

68 – 39

Count on from 39 up to 68 to find the answer to the subtraction.

so 68 – 39 = 1 + 20 + 8 = 29

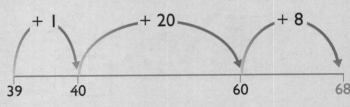

1 Work out the answer to each subtraction by completing the empty number line.

a 74 – 45 = 29

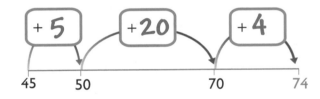

b 86 – 43 =

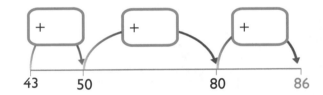

c 53 – 39 =

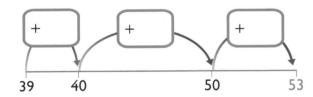

d 94 – 46 =

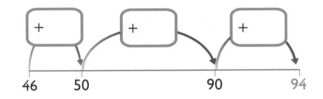

e 47 – 18 =

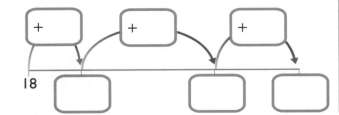

f 91 – 35 =

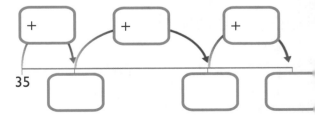

2 Subtract each pair of numbers. Use the number line to work out the answer.

a 78 – 35 = 43

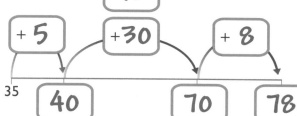

b 65 – 24 =

c 77 – 48 =

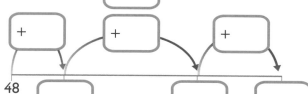

d 56 – 37 =

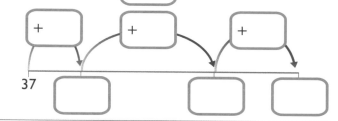

e 63 – 19 =

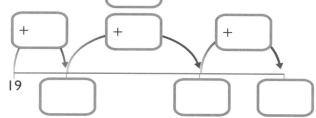

f 91 – 57 =

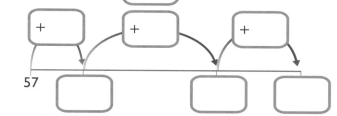

g 83 – 46 =

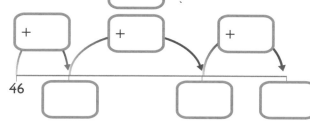

h 92 – 74 =

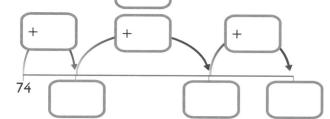

◆ I can subtract a two-digit number from another two-digit number using an empty number line.

Let's try this!

Choose numbers on two flowers.
Subtract the smaller number
from the larger number.
Repeat this for different flowers.
What are the largest and smallest
differences you can make?

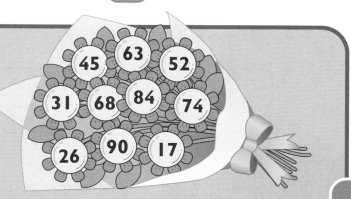

Subtracting a two-digit number from a three-digit number

● I can subtract a two-digit number from a three-digit number using an empty number line.

Key words
subtract, add, digits, number line, difference

Here is a way to subtract a two-digit number from a three-digit number using a number line.

Write the two-digit number at the start of the number line.

156 – 77

Count on from 77 up to 156.

so 156 – 77 = 3 + 20 + 50 + 6 = 79

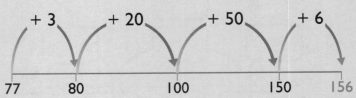

1 Work out the answer to each subtraction by completing the empty number line.

a 150 – 21 = [129]

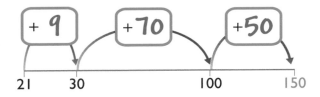

b 140 – 65 = [ ]

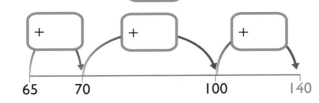

c 156 – 70 = [ ]

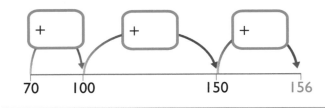

d 143 – 78 = [ ]

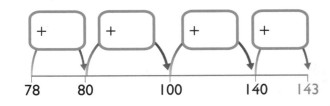

e 191 – 35 = [ ]

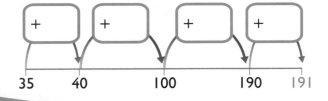

f 240 – 68 = [ ]

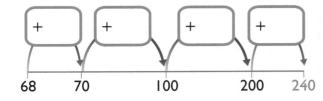

2 Subtract each pair of numbers. Use the number line to work out the answer.

a 160 – 92 = [68]

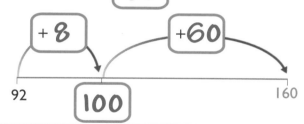

+8   +60

92   100   160

b 128 – 69 = [ ]

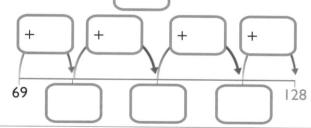

+   +   +   +

69   128

c 189 – 58 = [ ]

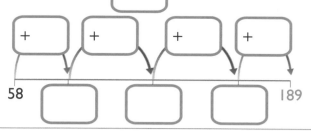

+   +   +   +

58   189

d 280 – 86 = [ ]

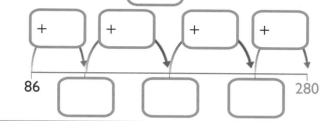

+   +   +   +

86   280

e 210 – 77 = [ ]

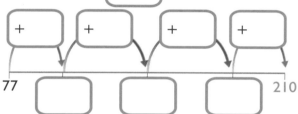

+   +   +   +

77   210

f 228 – 56 = [ ]

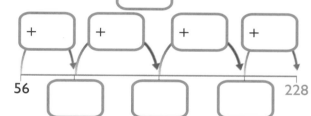

+   +   +   +

56   228

g 310 – 47 = [ ]

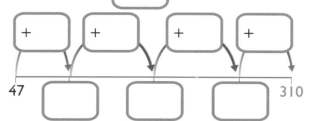

+   +   +   +

47   310

h 355 – 66 = [ ]

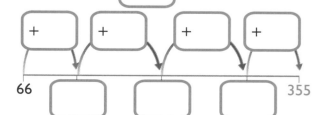

+   +   +   +

66   355

 I can subtract a two-digit number from a three-digit number using an empty number line. [ ]

Let's try this!

Choose a two-digit number and a three-digit number. Find the difference between the two numbers. Repeat this for different pairs of numbers.

136   185   27   38
263   341   79   52

4.1 Six and eight times tables

● I know the six and eight times tables.

Key words
multiplication, times tables

Here are the multiplication facts for the eight times table.

$1 \times 8 = 8$

$2 \times 8 = 16$

$3 \times 8 = 24$

$4 \times 8 = 32$

$5 \times 8 = 40$

$6 \times 8 = 48$

$7 \times 8 = 56$

$8 \times 8 = 64$

$9 \times 8 = 72$

$10 \times 8 = 80$

1 Now work out the six times table.

a $\boxed{1} \times 6 = \boxed{6}$

b $\boxed{2} \times 6 = \boxed{12}$

c  $\boxed{} \times 6 = \boxed{}$

d $\boxed{} \times 6 = \boxed{}$

e $\boxed{} \times 6 = \boxed{}$

f $\boxed{} \times 6 = \boxed{}$

g $\boxed{} \times 6 = \boxed{}$

h $\boxed{} \times 6 = \boxed{}$

i $\boxed{} \times 6 = \boxed{}$

j $\boxed{} \times 6 = \boxed{}$

2 Complete these multiplication facts from the six and eight times tables.

a $2 \times 6 =$ 12

b $4 \times 8 =$ ☐

c $5 \times 6 =$ ☐

d ☐ $\times 6 = 42$

e ☐ $\times 8 = 48$

f ☐ $\times 6 = 60$

g ☐ $\times 8 = 72$

h ☐ $\times 8 = 24$

i ☐ $\times 6 = 24$

3 Each number that goes into the machine is multiplied by either 6 or 8.
Fill in the missing numbers.

a

b
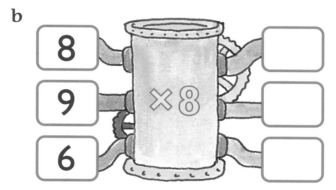

c
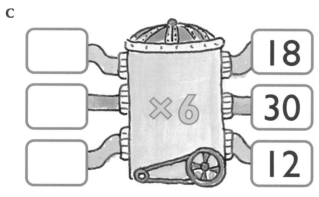

d
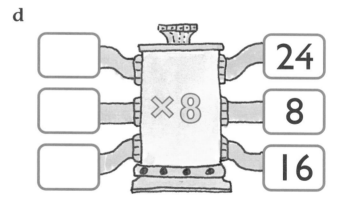

◆ I know the six and eight times tables. ☐

Let's try this!

Write out the **four** times table. Did you know that if you double the answers to the four times table you get the eight times table? Check that this is true.

Seven and nine times tables

● I know the seven and nine times tables.

Key words
multiplication, times tables

Multiplication facts for the seven and nine times tables.

$1 \times 7 = 7$	$1 \times 9 = 9$
$2 \times 7 = 14$	$2 \times 9 = 18$
$3 \times 7 = 21$	$3 \times 9 = 27$
$4 \times 7 = 28$	$4 \times 9 = 36$
$5 \times 7 = 35$	$5 \times 9 = 45$
$6 \times 7 = 42$	$6 \times 9 = 54$
$7 \times 7 = 49$	$7 \times 9 = 63$
$8 \times 7 = 56$	$8 \times 9 = 72$
$9 \times 7 = 63$	$9 \times 9 = 81$
$10 \times 7 = 70$	$10 \times 9 = 90$

1 Complete each multiplication fact for the nine times table.

a
$1 \times 9 = \boxed{9}$

$5 \times 9 = \boxed{}$

$10 \times 9 = \boxed{}$

$2 \times 9 = \boxed{}$

b
$3 \times 9 = \boxed{}$

$7 \times 9 = \boxed{}$

$8 \times 9 = \boxed{}$

$6 \times 9 = \boxed{}$

c
$\boxed{} \times 9 = 27$

$\boxed{} \times 9 = 54$

$\boxed{} \times 9 = 45$

$\boxed{} \times 9 = 81$

2 Complete each multiplication fact for the seven times table.

a
2 × 7 = 14
5 × 7 = ☐
1 × 7 = ☐
10 × 7 = ☐

b
3 × 7 = ☐
4 × 7 = ☐
9 × 7 = ☐
7 × 7 = ☐

c
☐ × 7 = 28
☐ × 7 = 63
☐ × 7 = 49
☐ × 7 = 77

3 Find a path through the number grid that only uses answers to the seven times table.
Colour the squares that make the correct path.

start

21	28	35	17	60	2
1	3	42	20	13	9
12	11	7	70	66	15
50	16	22	14	55	41
5	4	33	49	56	63

finish

4 Find a path through the number grid that only uses answers to the nine times table.
Colour the squares that make the correct path.

finish

1	22	6	7	81	63
30	72	54	45	27	51
20	18	41	25	13	15
36	90	40	31	2	39
9	33	11	47	4	5

start

 I know the seven and nine times tables. ☐

Let's try this!

Choose a number. Write down two multiplication facts from the times tables that have this number as the answer. For example, for 18: 2 × 9 and 3 × 6.

4.3 Multiplying and dividing by 10

- I can multiply and divide whole numbers by 10.

Key words
multiply, divide

When a number is **multiplied** by 10, each digit becomes ten times bigger.

4 tens, 3 units ⟶ $43 \times 10 = 430$ ⟵ 4 hundreds, 3 tens, 0 units

The number 4 moves from 4 tens to 4 hundreds.
The number 3 moves from 3 units to 3 tens.
A zero must be added at the end, which is the units number.

When a number is **divided** by 10, each digit becomes ten times smaller.

$$5840 \div 10 = 584$$

The number 5 moves from 5 thousands to 5 hundreds.
The number 8 moves from 8 hundreds to 8 tens.
The number 4 moves from 4 tens to 4 units.
(Notice it looks like a zero has simply been removed from the end.)

1 Multiply each number by 10

a 70 → 700

b 63 →

c 98 →

d 160 →

e 176 →

f 290 →

2 Divide each number by 10

a
 12

b

c

d

e

f
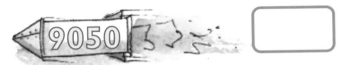

3 Write the correct sign to complete the multiplications and divisions.

a 65 ⎡ X ⎤ 10 = 650

b 520 ☐ 10 = 52

c 265 ☐ 10 = 2650

d 800 ☐ 10 = 80

e 600 ☐ 10 = 6000

f 5400 ☐ 10 = 540

g 1290 ☐ 10 = 129

h 690 ☐ 10 = 6900

I can multiply and divide whole numbers by 10. ☐

Let's try this!

Here is a number machine that multiplies numbers by 10. Write five inputs and outputs for this machine. Now draw a number machine that divides numbers by 10. Write five inputs and outputs.

inputs
652
54
627
8

outputs
6520
540
6270
80

Multiplying a two-digit number by a one-digit number

● I can multiply a two-digit number by 2, 3, 4 or 5.

Key words
multiply, multiple

To multiply a multiple of 10 you can use your times tables:

$$40 \times 3$$

You know that $4 \times 3 = 12$
so $40 \times 3 = 120$

To multiply a two-digit number, first split it into tens and units:

$$23 \times 5$$

$20 \times 5 = 100$
$3 \times 5 = 15$
$23 \times 5 = 100 + 15 = 115$

1 Use the tables facts to work out these multiplications.

a $30 \times 4 =$ 120

b $90 \times 5 =$

c $80 \times 3 =$

d $90 \times 4 =$

2 Fill in the boxes.

a 29×2 $20 \times 2 =$ 40
                 $9 \times 2 =$ 18
$29 \times 2 =$ 40 $+$ 18 $=$ 58

b 42×5 $40 \times 5 =$
                  $2 \times 5 =$
$42 \times 5 =$ $+$ $=$

c 38 × 4 30 × 4 = ☐

8 × 4 = ☐

38 × 4 = ☐ + ☐ = ☐

d 82 × 3 80 × 3 = ☐

2 × 3 = ☐

82 × 3 = ☐ + ☐ = ☐

e 54 × 5 50 × 5 = ☐

4 × 5 = ☐

54 × 5 = ☐ + ☐ = ☐

f 69 × 3 60 × 3 = ☐

9 × 3 = ☐

69 × 3 = ☐ + ☐ = ☐

3 Work out the answer to each multiplication.

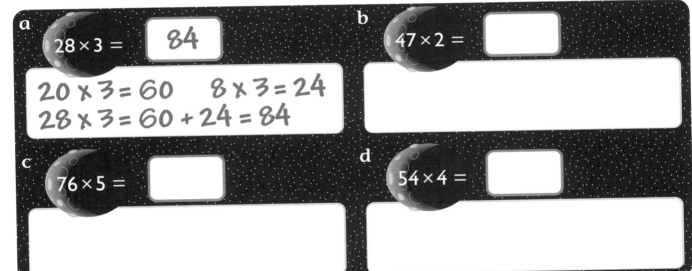

a 28 × 3 = 84

20 × 3 = 60   8 × 3 = 24
28 × 3 = 60 + 24 = 84

b 47 × 2 = ☐

c 76 × 5 = ☐

d 54 × 4 = ☐

 I can multiply a two-digit number by 2, 3, 4 or 5. ☐

Let's try this!

Choose two digit cards from 0–9 to make a two-digit number. Choose one of these multiplication cards and work out the answer to the multiplication. Try it again with a different two-digit number.

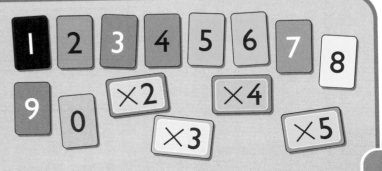

● I can divide a two-digit number by 2, 3, 4 or 5 and find the remainder.

Key words
divide, remainder

Remember that you can find division facts if you know times tables.

$21 \div 3$

Use the fact that $7 \times 3 = 21$ so $21 \div 3 = 7$

Sometimes a number cannot be divided exactly.
You get an answer and a **remainder**.

$22 \div 5$

Use the fact that $20 \div 5 = 4$ so $22 \div 5 = 4 \text{ r } 2$
(r is short for remainder)

1 Use the times tables facts to work out these divisions.

a $12 \div 3 = \boxed{4}$ b $16 \div 4 = \boxed{}$ c $20 \div 2 = \boxed{}$

d $25 \div 5 = \boxed{}$ e $21 \div 3 = \boxed{}$ f $45 \div 5 = \boxed{}$

g $36 \div 4 = \boxed{}$ h $24 \div 3 = \boxed{}$ i $28 \div 4 = \boxed{}$

2 Work out the answer and remainder for each division.

a

16   $\boxed{15 \div 5 = 3}$ so $\boxed{16 \div 5 = 3 \text{ r } 1}$

24   $\boxed{}$ so $\boxed{}$

36   $\boxed{}$ so $\boxed{}$

47   $\boxed{}$ so $\boxed{}$

b ÷3

16 [ ] so [ ]

7 [ ] so [ ]

32 [ ] so [ ]

c ÷4

9 [ ] so [ ]

30 [ ] so [ ]

22 [ ] so [ ]

3 Each piece of fruit has a number inside. Work out the divisions. Some have remainders but some do not.

19 13 8 20 16 18 24 24 50 30 32 7 6 36

a Divide the oranges by 3 | 24÷3=8 | 18÷3=6 | 6÷3=2 |

b Divide the bananas by 5   [ ] [ ] [ ]

c Divide the pears by 4   [ ] [ ] [ ]

d Divide the melons by 2   [ ] [ ] [ ]

e Divide the apples by 5   [ ] [ ] [ ]

 I can divide a two-digit number by 2, 3, 4 or 5 and find the remainder. [ ]

Let's try this!

Choose a number card and a division card.
Work out the answer to the division.
Repeat this for a different pair of cards.
How many divide exactly without a remainder?

÷3 15 20 ÷2

÷5 ÷4 19 24

MONEY

5.1 Pounds and pence

- I know that there are 100 pennies in one pound.
- I can use £1 and £2 coins.

Key words
coin, pound, pence, pennies, value

Here is a £1 coin.
It is worth 100 pence or 100 pennies.

£1 = 100p

Here is a £2 coin.
It is worth 200 pence or 200 pennies.

£2 = 200p

Here is a purse containing some £1 and £2 coins.

The total value of the coins is £7 or 700p.

1 Write the total value of the coins in each purse.

a

£ [6] = [600] p

b

£ [ ] = [ ] p

c
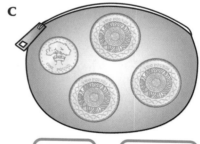
£ [ ] = [ ] p

d
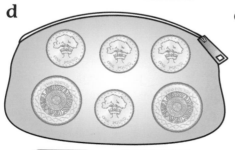
£ [ ] = [ ] p

e
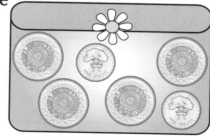
£ [ ] = [ ] p

f
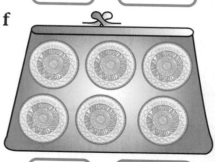
£ [ ] = [ ] p

2 You can use £1 and £2 coins to buy each box of fruit. Write the coins that you could use to pay exactly. You must use the least number of coins.

apples £5 lemons £7 grapes £4 mangoes £10 oranges £13

a Apples £5 = £2 + £2 + £1   b Lemons [   ]

c Grapes [   ]   d Mangoes [   ]

e Oranges [   ]

3 Here are some things you can buy in a garden centre.

a How much does it cost to buy a rose bush and a set of tools? £10

b How much does it cost to buy a hose and a rose bush? [   ]

c How much does it cost to buy two climbing plants? [   ]

d How much more does it cost to buy a rose bush than a gardening book? [   ]

e How much does it cost to buy two rose bushes and a climbing plant? [   ]

£14 £6 £3 £11 £4

◆ I know that there are 100 pennies in one pound and I can use £1 and £2 coins. [   ]

Let's try this!

Work out all of the ways you could pay exactly for the book using only £1 and £2 coins.

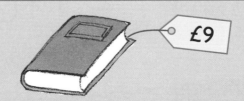

£9

5.2 Making pounds using other coins

● I can make amounts in pounds using other coins.

Key words
coin, pound, pence, total

Remember that £1 is equal to 100 pence.
You can use different coins to make a total of 100p.

£1 = 50p + 50p

£1 = 50p + 20p + 20p + 10p

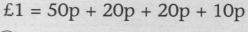

1 Write the number of coins it takes to make £1.

a
 £1 = | 100 | 1p coins

b
£1 = | | 2p coins

c
£1 = | | 5p coins

d
£1 = | | 10p coins

e
£1 = | | 20p coins

f
£1 = | | 50p coins

2 Tick the sets of coins that have a total value of £1.

a

b

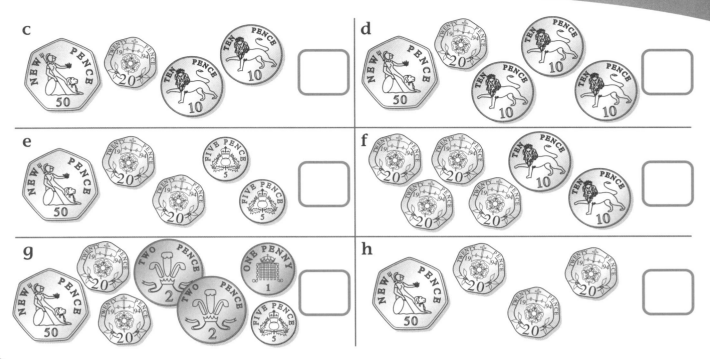

c   [ ]

d   [ ]

e   [ ]

f   [ ]

g   [ ]

h   [ ]

3 Write the values of coins that are needed to make a total of £2.

a   £2 = £1 + 50p + [50p]

b   £2 = £1 + 20p + 20p + 20p + [   ] + [   ]

c   £2 = 50p + 50p + 50p + [   ]

d   £2 = £1 + 50p + 10p + 10p + [   ] + [   ] + [   ]

e   £2 = 50p + 50p + 50p + 20p + 20p + [   ] + [   ]

f   £2 = £1 + 50p + 20p + 20p + 5p + [   ] + [   ] + [   ]

◆ I can make amounts in pounds using other coins.   [ ]

Let's try this!

Work out all the ways you can make £1 using no more than six coins.

Pounds and pence decimal notation

- I can write an amount in pounds and pence using decimals.

Key words
pound, pence, decimal point, value

Here are some coins with a total value of 174p that is the same as £1 and 74p. This is written in decimals as £1.74.

The pounds and pence are separated by a **decimal point**.

These coins have a total value of 57p. This is written in decimals as £0.57. The zero shows that there are no pounds.

These coins have a total value of 405p. This is written in decimals as £4.05.

1 Write the total value of each set of coins.

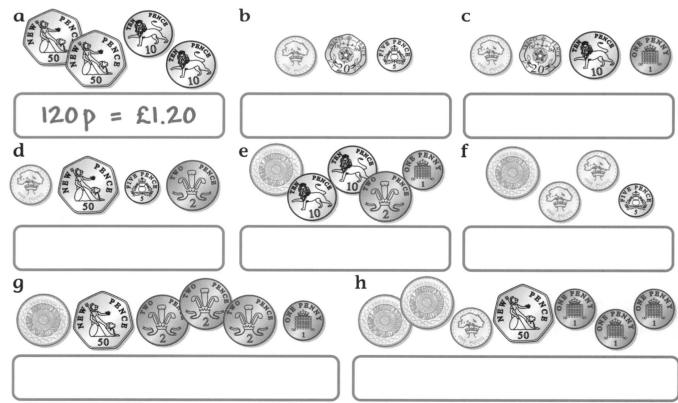

a
120p = £1.20

b

c

d

e

f

g

h

2 Write the price of each book in pence.

a   b   c   d   e

£1.92   £5.04   £8.50   £0.64   £0.08

192 p   ☐ p   ☐ p   ☐ p   ☐ p

3 Write the price of each thing in pounds.

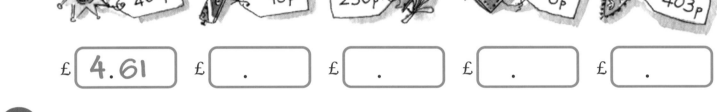

a   b   c   d   e

461p   95p   230p   6p   403p

£ 4.61   £ ☐ . ☐   £ ☐ . ☐   £ ☐ . ☐   £ ☐ . ☐

4 Write the price of the pen that costs the most.

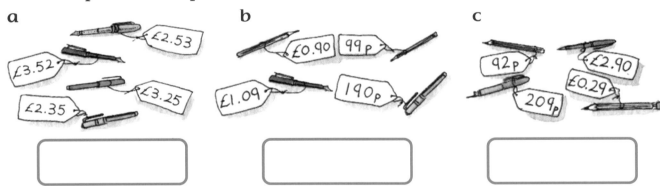

a   b   c

£2.53   £3.52   £3.25   £2.35   £0.90   99p   £1.09   190p   92p   £2.90   £0.29   209p

☐   ☐   ☐

◆ I can write an amount in pounds and pence using decimals. ☐

Let's try this!

Get some coins of different values. Choose six coins and work out the total value. Write the value in pence then in pounds. Repeat this for six different coins.

5.4 Addition problems with money

● I can add amounts of money.

Key words
altogether, total, cost

sandwich £2.15

smoothie £1.43

apple juice 90p

bananas 74p

Max buys an apple juice and some bananas. He works out the total cost.

90p + 74p = 164p This is written in pounds as £1.64.

Sanjit buys a sandwich and a smoothie. He works out the total cost.

£2.15 + £1.43 = £2 + £1 + 15p + 43p = £3 + 58p = £3.58

1 These things are for sale in a shop. Find the total cost of:

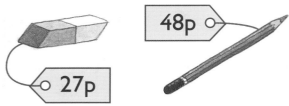

48p

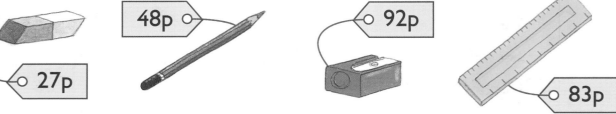

27p

92p

83p

a a rubber and a pencil

27p + 48p = 75p

b a pencil and a sharpener

c a ruler and a rubber

d a pencil and a ruler

e two sharpeners

f two rulers

2 These items are for sale in a charity shop. Find the total cost of:

a a torch and a teapot

£1.58 + £1.40 = £2.98

b a game and a calculator

c a TV and a lamp

d a calculator and a torch

e a teapot and a game

f a lamp and a calculator

3 Work out the total cost of each set.

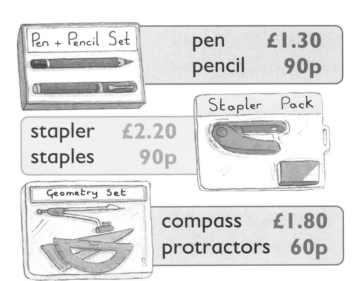

pen £1.30
pencil 90p

stapler £2.20
staples 90p

compass £1.80
protractors 60p

a Pen and pencil set

b Stapler pack

c Geometry set

◆ I can add amounts of money.

Let's try this!

Choose two price labels and find the total cost.

£1.35   £2.33   £0.72

£0.08   £3.67   £0.41

● I can work out the change when buying something.

Here are some of the coins and notes we use every day.

Pete buys a pizza for £3.75.

He pays for it with a £5 note.

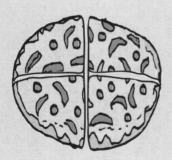

What is his change?

£5 – £3.75 = 25p + £1.00 = £1.25

Pete's change is £1.25.

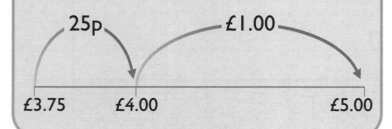

25p   £1.00

£3.75   £4.00   £5.00

1 Milly buys a 75p stamp for her parcel. Work out the change she would get if she paid with these coins or notes.

a   b

25p

c

d

2 These things are for sale in a clothes shop. Work out the change you would get if you bought each one using a £5 note.

£3.92 £4.66 £2.30 £1.29

a Jeans

£5 — £3.92 = £1.08

b Shirt

c Jumper

d T-shirt

3 Aanya buys some things for her holiday. How much change will she get when she pays for each thing with the money shown?

£5.82 £4.25 £2.18 £7.59

a Sunglasses bought with a £5 note

£5 — £4.25 = 75p

b Sunscreen bought with two £2 coins

c Flip-flops bought with a £5 note and a £2 coin

d Sun-hat bought with a £10 note

 I can work out the change when buying something.

Let's try this!

Choose two price labels and find the total value.
Work out the change you would get if you paid with a £5 note.
Repeat this for different price tags.

£1.19 £1.52 £2.60 £1.79 £2.17 £2.36

MEASURE – LENGTH AND TIME
6.1 Measuring in millimetres

● I can measure a length using centimetres and millimetres.

Key words
centimetre (cm), measure, millimetre (mm)

A centimetre is divided into 10 smaller units called millimetres.

So **1 cm = 10 mm**

The key measures:

4 cm 9 mm = 40 mm + 9 mm
= 49 mm

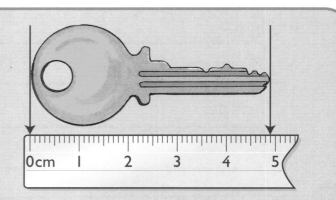

1 Get a ruler. Measure these things to the nearest millimetre. Write the length below the line.

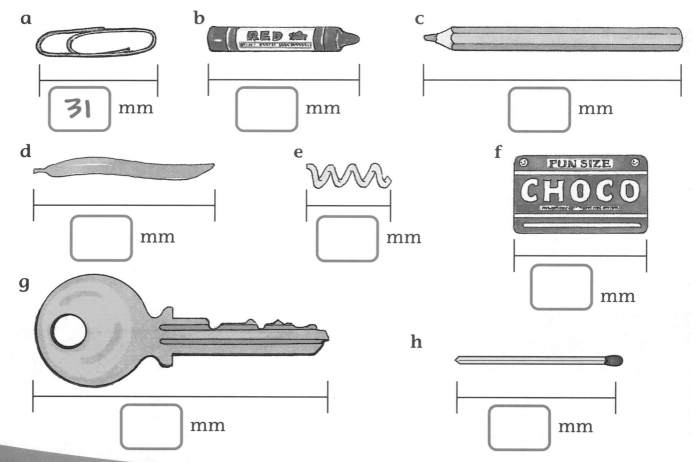

a [31] mm

b [ ] mm

c [ ] mm

d [ ] mm

e [ ] mm

f [ ] mm

g [ ] mm

h [ ] mm

2 Get a ruler.

   a Measure the sides of the square in millimetres.

     Side AB = [ ] mm

   b Draw a line to join A to C.

     Line AC = [ ] mm

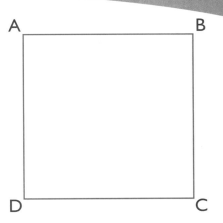

3 **a** Measure the sides of the hexagon in millimetres.

     Side AB = [ ] mm

     = [ ] cm [ ] mm

   b Draw a line to join B to D.

     Line BD = [ ] mm

     = [ ] cm [ ] mm

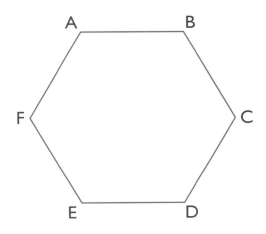

◆ I can measure a length to the nearest millimetre and I know that 1 cm = 10 mm. [ ]

Let's try this!

   a Write the lengths shown on this ruler in decimals.

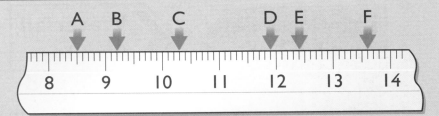

   A [85] mm = [8·5] cm   B [ ] mm = [ ] cm

   C [ ] mm = [ ] cm   D [ ] mm = [ ] cm

   E [ ] mm = [ ] cm   F [ ] mm = [ ] cm

   b Find the distance from A to E in centimetres. [ ] cm

- I know how many centimetres make 1 metre.
- I know how many metres make 1 kilometre.

Key words
kilometre (km), metre (m), centimetre (cm), length, distance

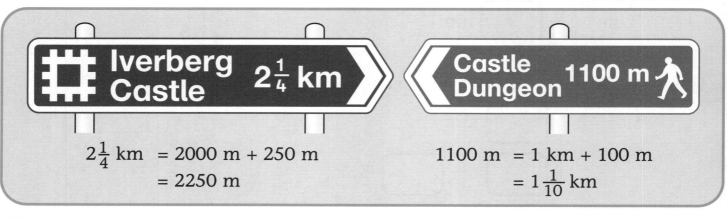

$2\frac{1}{4}$ km = 2000 m + 250 m
= 2250 m

1100 m = 1 km + 100 m
= $1\frac{1}{10}$ km

1 Fill in the table.

Kilometres	1 km	$\frac{1}{2}$ km	$\frac{1}{4}$ km	$\frac{1}{10}$ km	
Metres	1000 m				750 m

2 Look at each signpost and write the distance in kilometres or metres.

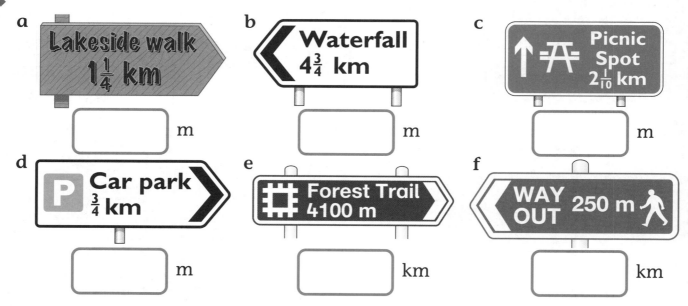

a Lakeside walk $1\frac{1}{4}$ km
☐ m

b Waterfall $4\frac{3}{4}$ km
☐ m

c Picnic Spot $2\frac{1}{10}$ km
☐ m

d Car park $\frac{3}{4}$ km
☐ m

e Forest Trail 4100 m
☐ km

f WAY OUT 250 m
☐ km

3 Fill in the tables.

a

Metres	1 m	$\frac{1}{2}$ m	$\frac{1}{4}$ m		$\frac{3}{4}$ m
Centimetres	100 cm			10 cm	

b

Metres	0.2 m		0.7 m		0.9 m		0.6 m
Centimetres	20 cm	50 cm		40 cm		80 cm	

4 Change these distances to metres.

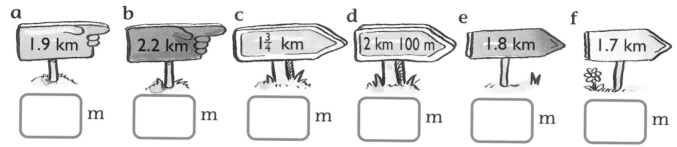

a 1.9 km ☐ m

b 2.2 km ☐ m

c 1$\frac{3}{4}$ km ☐ m

d 2 km 100 m ☐ m

e 1.8 km ☐ m

f 1.7 km ☐ m

g Now put the distances in order starting with the shortest.

 I know how many centimetres make 1 metre and how many metres make 1 kilometre. ☐

Let's try this!

Mandy and Jenny live in the same street. Mandy's house is 800 m from Jenny's house. There is a lamp post in front of each girl's house and three lamp posts in-between. All lamp posts are the same distance apart.

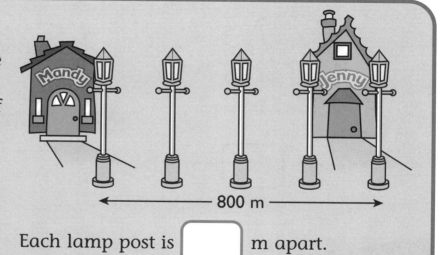

800 m

How far apart, in metres, is each lamp post?

Each lamp post is ☐ m apart.

6.3 Perimeter

● I can work out the perimeter of rectangles and squares.

The perimeter of a shape is the distance all the way round its edges.

Perimeter of rectangle = (3 + 2 + 3 + 2) cm

                   = 10 cm

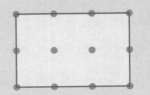

1 The dots on the edges of these rectangles are 1 cm apart.
Find the perimeter of each rectangle in centimetres.

a

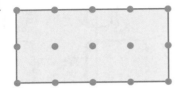

Perimeter [12] cm

b

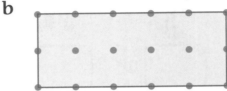

Perimeter [ ] cm

c

Perimeter [ ] cm

d

Perimeter [ ] cm

e

Perimeter [ ] cm

2 Get a ruler.
Two sides of these rectangles have been drawn. Complete each rectangle.

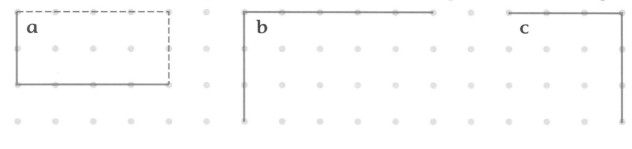

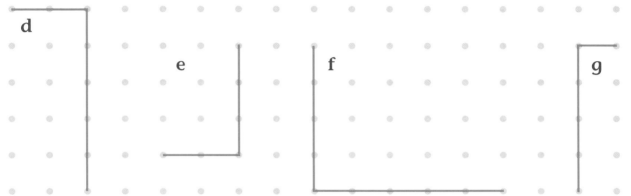

Write their perimeters in centimetres in the table.

Rectangle	a	b	c	d	e	f	g
Perimeter	12 cm	cm	cm	cm	cm	cm	cm

◆ I can work out the perimeter of rectangles and squares.

Let's try this!

These shapes are made with five square tiles. Each square has sides of 1 cm.
Find the perimeter of each shape.

a
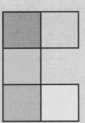

b
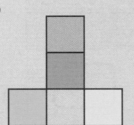

c
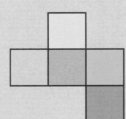

- I can calculate the area of shapes by counting squares.

Key words
area, square, rectangle, centimetre (cm), square centimetres

Area is the space inside a shape.
We measure area in square centimetres.

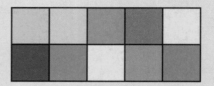

Area of rectangle = 10 square cm

1 Count the number of coloured squares in each rectangle to find its area.

a

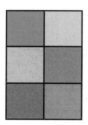

Area = 6 square cm

b

Area = ☐ square cm

c

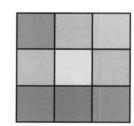

Area = ☐ square cm

d

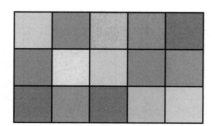

Area = ☐ square cm

e

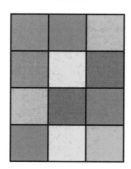

Area = ☐ square cm

f

Area = ☐ square cm

2 Count the number of green squares in each shape and write its area.

a = ⬜ square cm

b = ⬜ square cm

c = ⬜ square cm

d = ⬜ square cm

e = ⬜ square cm

3 Draw the missing sides of each rectangle so that the shape matches its area.

a 12 square cm   b 15 square cm   c 16 square cm

◆ I can calculate the area of shapes by counting squares. ⬜

Let's try this!

A   B   C   D

Look at the squares A to D. Draw the next square in the pattern and label it E.

Area of E = ⬜ square cm   Perimeter of E = ⬜ cm

6.5 | Time to the minute

- I can tell the time to the nearest minute on a clock with hands.
- I can tell the time on a 12-hour digital clock.

Key words
minutes (min), hours (h), digital

This clock shows
26 minutes past 10
or 10:26

This clock shows
8 minutes to 2
or 1:52

1 Write these times in two ways.

a

[27] min past [3]

[3 : 27]

b

[ ] min past [ ]

[:]

c

[ ] min past [ ]

[:]

d

[ ] min to [ ]

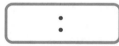

[:]

e

[ ] min to [ ]

[:]

f

[ ] min to [ ]

[:]

g

[ ] min past [ ]

[:]

h

[ ] min to [ ]

[:]

2 Write these times in two ways.

a 3:43 [43] minutes past [3]   [17] minutes to [4]

b 4:58 [   ] minutes past [   ]   [   ] minutes to [   ]

c 7:46 [   ] minutes past [   ]   [   ] minutes to [   ]

d 9:51 [   ] minutes past [   ]   [   ] minutes to [   ]

e 10:47 [   ] minutes past [   ]   [   ] minutes to [   ]

3 This clock shows 14 minutes past 6 `6:14`   This clock shows 2 minutes to 6 `5:58`

Write the time these digital clocks show.

a `2:07`   b `8:26`   c `4:12`

d `11:44`   e `4:36`   f `12:52`

◆ I can tell the time to the nearest minute on a clock with hands and on a 12-hour digital clock. [   ]

Let's try this!

Look at the time on this clock.
Write the digital time: `9:03`

a 5 minutes earlier

b in 3 hours' time

c 20 minutes later

d half an hour ago

[:]   [:]   [:]   [:]

UNDERSTANDING SHAPES

7.1 More or less than a right angle

● I can test whether an angle is equal to, more than or less than a right angle.

Key words
angle, right angle, acute, obtuse, set square

Look at the handles of these fans.

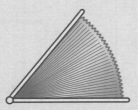 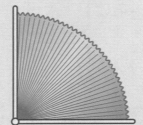 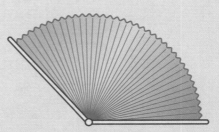

The handles make an angle less than a right angle.

This is an **acute angle**.

The handles make a **right angle**.

The handles make an angle more than a right angle.

This is an **obtuse angle**.

---

1 Use a set square to test whether the handles of each fan make an angle which is less than or more than a right angle. Write your answers in the table.

Less than a right angle	
More than a right angle	

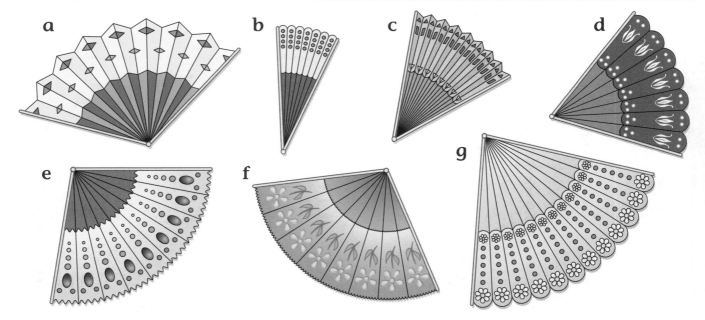

a   b   c   d

e   f   g

2 Check the measurement of these angles with a set square.
Colour the acute angles red and obtuse angles blue.

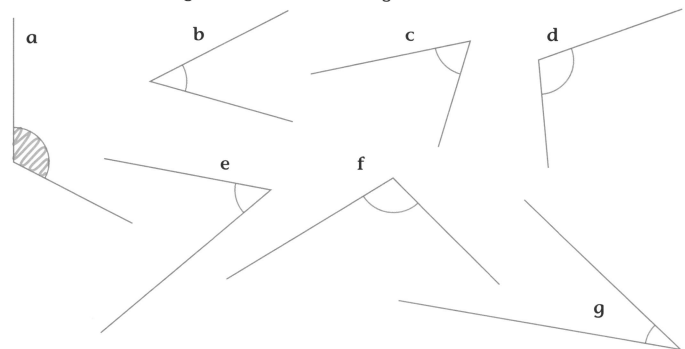

3 Name the marked angle in each of these shapes.

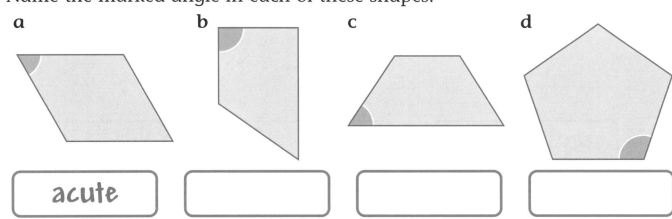

a
| acute |

b
| |

c
| |

d
| |

◆ I can test whether an angle is equal to,
more than or less than a right angle. ☐

Let's try this!

You will need
a 45°, 45°, 90° set square.
Which of these shapes
have two angles of 45°?

| |

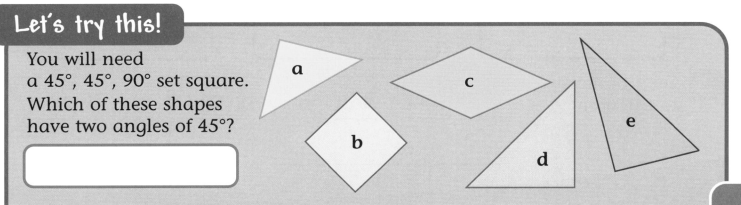

Equilateral and right-angled triangles

- I can recognise equilateral and right-angled triangles from other triangles.

Key words
triangle, angle, side, equilateral, right-angled triangle, set square

Equilateral triangles *have all sides equal.*

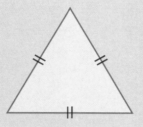

Right-angled triangles *have one right angle.*

1
a   Draw a straight line with a ruler to complete each triangle.
b   Use a set square to test for right angles. Write whether the triangle is equilateral, right-angled or other.

a

equilateral

b

c

d

e

f

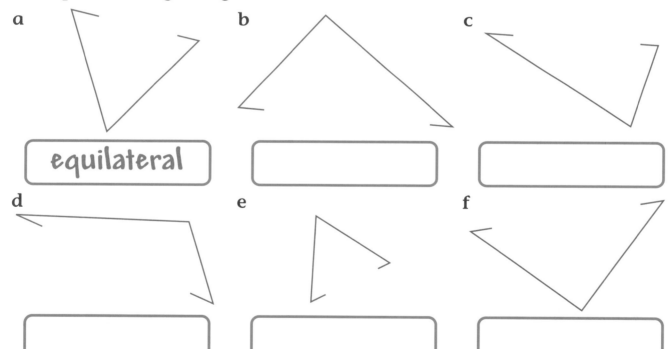

2 Sort your answers to Question 1.

Equilateral	Right-angled	Other
a		

3 Get a ruler and a set square. Sort these triangles and write the letter for each triangle in the boxes.

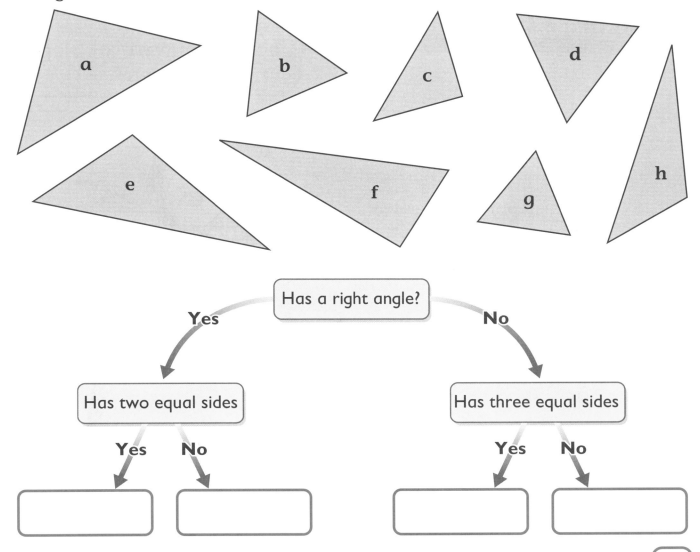

Has a right angle?

Yes   No

Has two equal sides   Has three equal sides

Yes   No   Yes   No

◆ I can recognise equilateral and right-angled triangles from other triangles.

You will need a paper cut-out in the shape of a square, scissors, ruler and 1 cm square dot paper.

Fold your square of paper diagonally and then diagonally again.

Cut out the four triangles.

Use all four triangles to make:

a a rectangle   **b** a square   **c** a right-angled triangle

Draw the three shapes on square dot paper.

Horizontal or vertical?

- I know when a line is horizontal or vertical.

Key words
horizontal, vertical, sloping, line of symmetry

In this picture

the ice floe is flat, level or **horizontal**.

The penguin is upright or **vertical**.

1 For each object write whether the red lines are horizontal or vertical.

a

horizontal

b

c

d

e

f

g

h
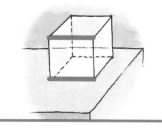

i

2 Look at the lines of symmetry. Write H for horizontal, V for vertical and S for sloping.

a

HANNAH ☐

b
T | T
A | A
X | X
I | I ☐

c
ARROW ☐

d
DESK ☐

e
ANDY ☐

f
TIM ☐

3 Get a ruler and blue, red and green pencils. Continue the pattern.
Colour horizontal lines blue, vertical lines red and sloping lines green.

◆ I know when a line is horizontal or vertical. ☐

Let's try this!

You can draw six CAPITAL letters using only horizontal or vertical lines.

Check if this statement is true or false.

On the square dot grid draw the capital letters using straight lines to connect the dots.

Regular or irregular shapes?

- I can use properties of 2-D shapes to sort them into sets.

Key words
property, regular, irregular, equilateral, right angle, rectangle, square, pentagon, hexagon, octagon, line of symmetry

Look at the two shapes.

A regular shape has:

- all sides equal

- all angles equal

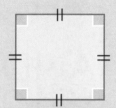
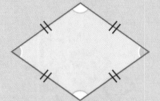

Four equal sides
Four equal angles
This is a regular shape

Four equal sides
Two pairs of equal angles
This is an irregular shape

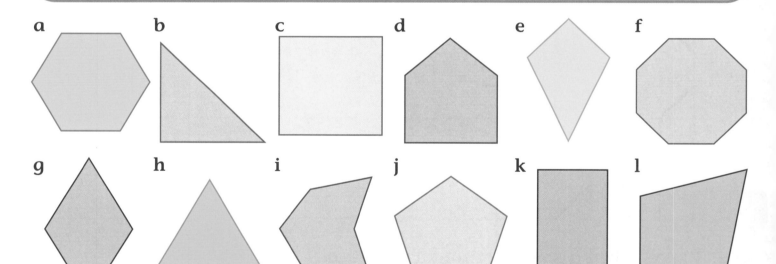

1 Write the letters of the 2-D shapes in these boxes.

a

Regular	Irregular
a	

b

Has a right angle	Has no right angle

2 Look at the set of 2-D shapes on page 70.
Write the letters of the 2-D shapes in these boxes.

a

	Regular	Irregular
Has three sides	h	
Has four sides		

b

	Regular	Irregular
Line symmetry		
No line symmetry		

3 Look at the set of 2-D shapes on page 70.
Write the letters of the 2-D shapes in these boxes.

Property	2-D shape
Has all sides equal	a
Has two or more right angles	
Has two or more lines of symmetry	

◆ I can use properties of 2-D shapes to sort them into sets. ☐

Let's try this!

Write the letter of each shape which has these properties.

Property	2-D shape
Has all sides equal	
Has one or more obtuse angles	
Has one or more lines of symmetry	

- I can complete a pattern and solve a problem about symmetry.

Key words
mirror line, line of symmetry, pattern, reflection, symmetrical

This is half of a pattern.

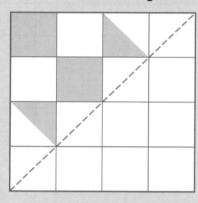

This is the pattern reflected in the line of symmetry.

The pattern has two lines of symmetry.

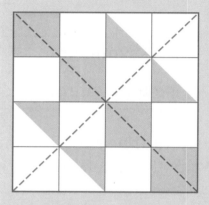

1 Get coloured pencils and a ruler.
Draw and colour the reflection of each pattern.
Find and rule the second line of symmetry with a red dotted line.

a

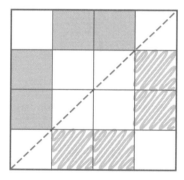

b

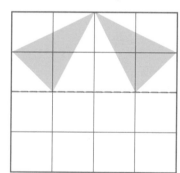

c

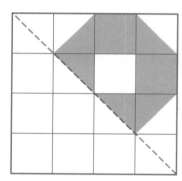

d

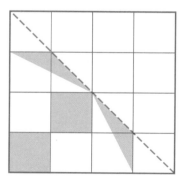

e

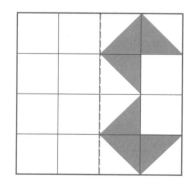

f

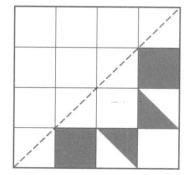

2 **a** Get a red and a blue pencil, a ruler and a mirror.
Each flag must have one red and one blue square. Each square must be all one colour. Make as many different flags as you can.

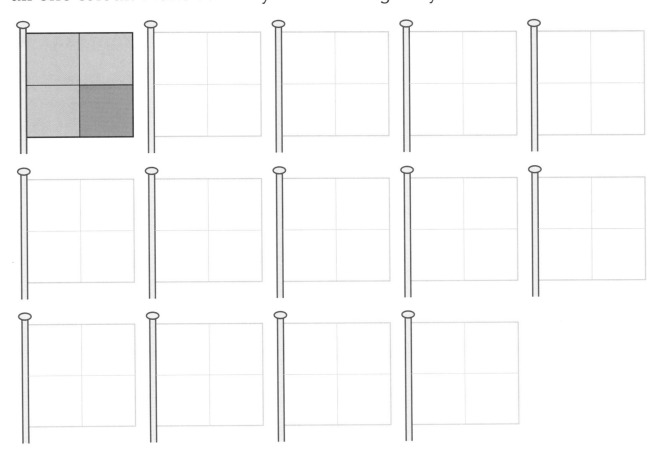

b Draw all the lines of symmetry for the flags above. How many flags have:

one line of symmetry? ☐   two lines of symmetry? ☐

◆ I can complete a symmetrical pattern and solve a puzzle about symmetry. ☐

Let's try this!

An equilateral triangle has three equal sides and three lines of symmetry.
Draw the lines of symmetry for these regular shapes.

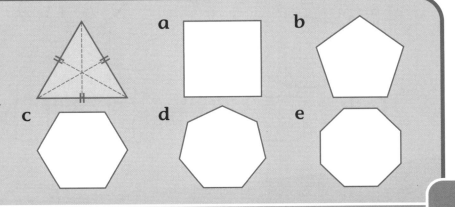

8.1 Grams and kilograms

● I can measure weight in grams and kilograms.

Key words
gram (g), kilogram (kg), weight, standard weight

1 kg = 1000 g

$\frac{1}{2}$ kg = 500 g

$\frac{1}{4}$ kg = 250 g

$\frac{1}{10}$ kg = 100 g

$4\frac{1}{4}$ kg = 4250 g

$1\frac{2}{10}$ kg = 1200 g

1 Write the weights shown on the scales in kilograms and in grams.

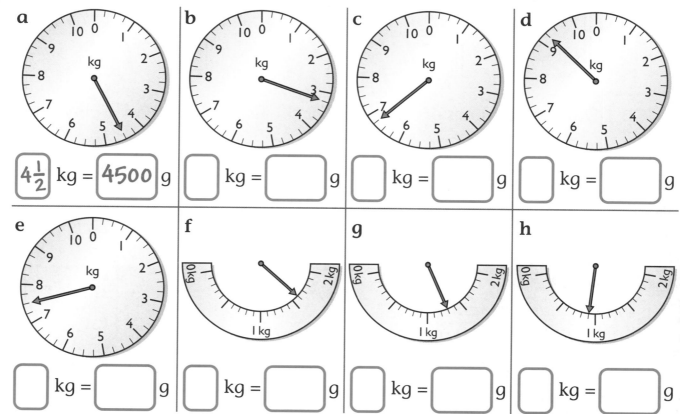

a $4\frac{1}{2}$ kg = 4500 g

b ☐ kg = ☐ g

c ☐ kg = ☐ g

d ☐ kg = ☐ g

e ☐ kg = ☐ g

f ☐ kg = ☐ g

g ☐ kg = ☐ g

h ☐ kg = ☐ g

2 Write the standard weight you would use to measure these things.

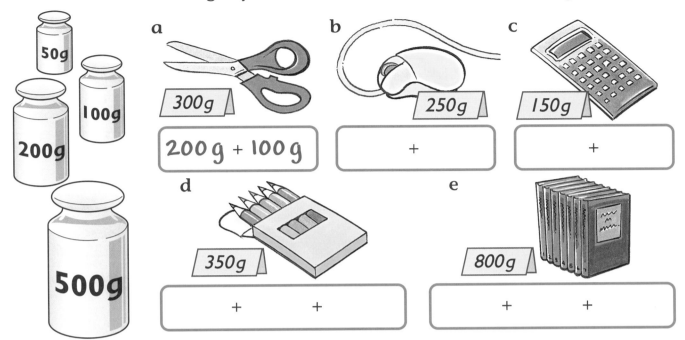

a

300g

$$200\,g + 100\,g$$

b

250g

+

c

150g

+

d

350g

+   +

e

800g

+   +

3 Change the weight of these parcels to grams.

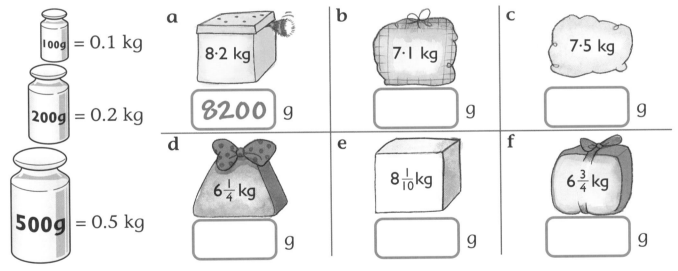

100g = 0.1 kg

200g = 0.2 kg

500g = 0.5 kg

a 8·2 kg

8200 g

b 7·1 kg

_____ g

c 7·5 kg

_____ g

d $6\frac{1}{4}$ kg

_____ g

e $8\frac{1}{10}$ kg

_____ g

f $6\frac{3}{4}$ kg

_____ g

◆ I can measure weight in grams and kilograms. ☐

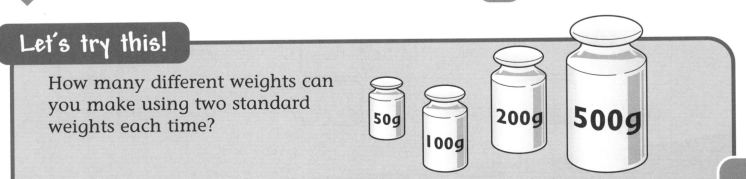

Let's try this!

How many different weights can you make using two standard weights each time?

50g   100g   200g   500g

Half and double quantities

● I can solve problems using grams.

Key words
gram (g), kilogram (kg), weight, half, double

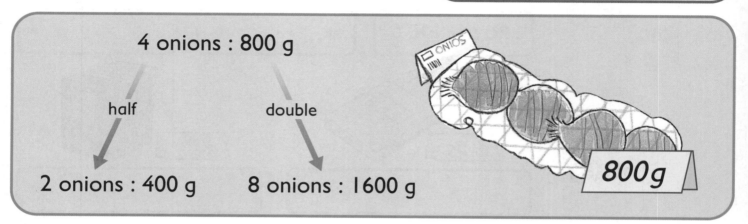

4 onions : 800 g

half

double

2 onions : 400 g

8 onions : 1600 g

800g

1 Find the weight of half and double of these foods.

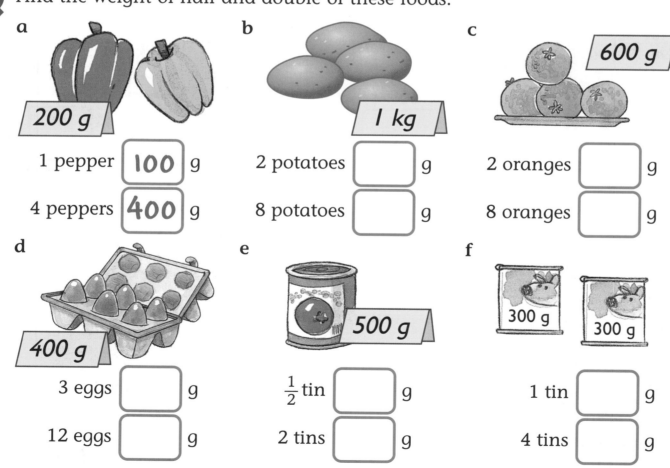

a

200 g

| 1 pepper | **100** g |
| 4 peppers | **400** g |

b

1 kg

| 2 potatoes | g |
| 8 potatoes | g |

c

600 g

| 2 oranges | g |
| 8 oranges | g |

d

400 g

| 3 eggs | g |
| 12 eggs | g |

e

500 g

| $\frac{1}{2}$ tin | g |
| 2 tins | g |

f

300 g   300 g

| 1 tin | g |
| 4 tins | g |

2 Write the recipes for two pies and for four pies.

Recipe for one pie	Recipe for two pies	Recipe for four pies
500 g apples	1000 g apples	___ g apples
300 g blueberries	___ g blueberries	___ g blueberries
100 g sugar	___ g sugar	___ g sugar
50 g butter	___ g butter	___ g butter
250 g flour	___ g flour	___ g flour

3 Look at the food in each shopping bag. Write the total weight of food in each bag.

a
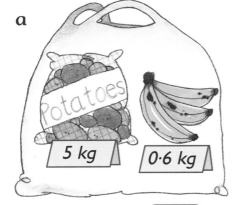
5 kg   0·6 kg

b
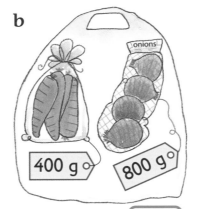
400 g   800 g

c

300 g   500 g

Total weight is ___ kg   Total weight is ___ g   Total weight is ___ g

 I can solve problems using grams. ___

Let's try this!

Look at the shopping bags in question 3. Write the weight of:

a one banana ___ g

b one carrot ___ g

c one onion ___ g

d two tins of chicken soup ___ g

e two bags of potatoes ___ kg

f four loaves of bread ___ kg

8.3 Fractions of a litre

● I know what $\frac{1}{2}$, $\frac{1}{4}$, $\frac{3}{4}$ and $\frac{1}{10}$ of 1 litre is in millilitres.

1

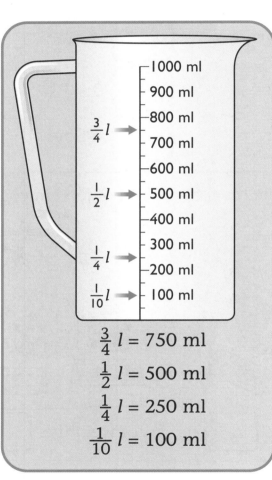

$\frac{3}{4}\,l$ = 750 ml

$\frac{1}{2}\,l$ = 500 ml

$\frac{1}{4}\,l$ = 250 ml

$\frac{1}{10}\,l$ = 100 ml

Fill in the boxes.

a 1 *l* = 500 ml + ⟦500⟧ ml = ⟦1000⟧ ml

b $\frac{1}{2}$ *l* = 250 ml + ⬚ ml = ⬚ ml

c $\frac{3}{4}$ *l* = ⬚ ml + 250 ml = ⬚ ml

d 1 *l* = 250 ml + ⬚ ml = ⬚ ml

e $\frac{2}{10}$ *l* = 100 ml + ⬚ ml = ⬚ ml

f $\frac{8}{10}$ *l* = 500 ml + ⬚ ml = ⬚ ml

g $\frac{6}{10}$ *l* = 100 ml + ⬚ ml = ⬚ ml

h $\frac{3}{4}$ *l* = ⬚ ml + ⬚ ml + 250 ml = ⬚ ml

2 Fill in the table. Write the capacity in litres or millilitres.

litres	0.1 *l*	0.2 *l*	0.3 *l*	⬚ *l*	⬚ *l*	0.8 *l*	⬚ *l*	1 *l*
millilitres	100 ml	⬚ ml	⬚ ml	500 ml	600 ml	⬚ ml	900 ml	⬚ ml

3 Write the capacity of each container in millilitres.

a

1.4 *l* = ☐ *l* ☐400☐ ml

= ☐1400☐ ml

b

2.5 *l* = ☐ *l* ☐ ml

= ☐ ml

c

4.2 *l* = ☐ *l* ☐ ml

= ☐ ml

d

3.1 *l* = ☐ *l* ☐ ml

= ☐ ml

e

2.8 *l* = ☐ *l* ☐ ml

= ☐ ml

f

5.3 *l* = ☐ *l* ☐ ml

= ☐ ml

g

2.7 *l* = ☐ *l* ☐ ml

= ☐ ml

h

3.9 *l* = ☐ *l* ☐ ml

= ☐ ml

i

6.6 *l* = ☐ *l* ☐ ml

= ☐ ml

 I know what $\frac{1}{2}$, $\frac{1}{4}$, $\frac{3}{4}$ and $\frac{1}{10}$ of 1 litre is in millilitres. ☐

Let's try this!

a The carton of milk holds ☐ ml.

b It will fill ☐ 250 ml mugs.

c It will fill ☐ 200 ml glasses.

Capacity problems

- I can record readings from scales and solve problems about capacity.

Key words
litre (*l*), millilitre (ml), capacity, container, measuring jug, scales

The measuring jars show the level before and after some water was poured out.

Amount poured out = 200 ml – 150 ml

= 50 ml

Before 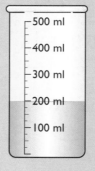 After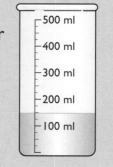

1 Write how many millilitres of water were poured out from each pair of jugs.

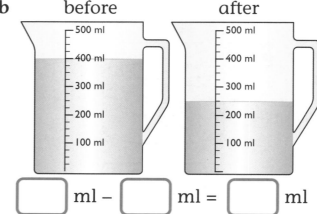

a before after

$\boxed{150}$ ml – $\boxed{100}$ ml = $\boxed{50}$ ml

b before after

$\boxed{}$ ml – $\boxed{}$ ml = $\boxed{}$ ml

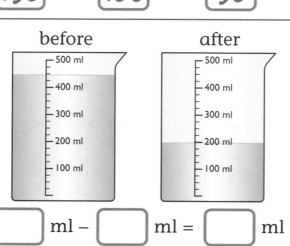

c before after

$\boxed{}$ ml – $\boxed{}$ ml = $\boxed{}$ ml

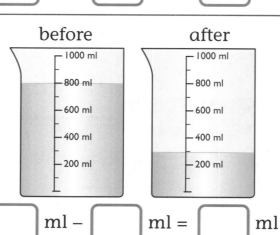

d before after

$\boxed{}$ ml – $\boxed{}$ ml = $\boxed{}$ ml

2 Write the capacity of each container in millilitres.

a
2·4 *l*
[2400] ml

b
$2\frac{1}{4}$ *l*
[   ] ml

c
3·5 *l*
[   ] ml

d
2·9 *l*
[   ] ml

e
$4\frac{4}{10}$ *l*
[   ] ml

f
3·8 *l*
[   ] ml

3 Find the number of times you can fill each measuring jug from the bottle beside it.

a
1 litre
100 ml
[   ] times

b
2 litres
250 ml
[   ] times

c
3 litres
500 ml
[   ] times

◆ I can record readings from scales and solve problems about capacity. [   ]

Let's try this!

A motorcyclist starts with a full tank of fuel.

a Write how much fuel is left in the tank:

- after trip A. [   ] litres
- after trip B. [   ] litres
- after trip C. [   ] litres

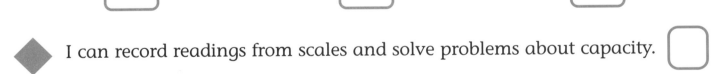

b How much fuel did he use? Trip A [   ] Trip B [   ] Trip C [   ]

● I can use a timetable and find a date on a calendar.

Key words
timetable, minutes (min), day, month, calendar, date

This timetable shows when a train leaves from one station and when it arrives at the next station.

The 10:15 train from Central Station arrives at Eastfield at 10:35.

Central Station	10:15
Westerton	10:25
Eastfield	10:35

1 The train takes 10 minutes between each station. Complete the train timetable.

Central Station	10:15	10:40	
Westerton	10:25		11:15
Eastfield	**10:35**		11:25
Southam		11:10	
Norby	10:55		

2 a How long is the journey from Central Station to Norby? ☐ min

b How long is the journey from Westerton to Southam? ☐ min

c You arrive at Westerton station at quarter to 11. In how many minutes' time will the train for Norby arrive? ☐ min

3 Look at the calendar for July 2009.

a How many days are:

Mondays? **4** Thursdays? ☐

Saturdays? ☐ Wednesdays? ☐

July 2009

S	M	T	W	Th	F	S
			1	2	3	4
5	6	7	8	9	10	11
12	13	14	15	16	17	18
19	20	21	22	23	24	25
26	27	28	29	30	31	

b Write the day of the week for:

14 July ☐

6 July ☐   25 July ☐

The first day in July ☐   The last day in July ☐

4 Here are some ways of writing the same date.

12 July 2009   12.07.2009   12/07/09
12.7.09   12.07.09

Choose three different ways to write:

a Today's date ☐

b Your birthday ☐

◆ I can use a timetable and find a date on a calendar. ☐

Let's try this!

Four friends have their birthday in July.

Use the clues to find the date of each friend's birthday.

● Danny first Monday   Date ☐

● Mary   last Wednesday   Date ☐

● Harry three days after Danny   Date ☐

● Sandy seven days before Mary   Date ☐

9.1 Picture 3-D shapes

● I can recognise solid shapes from
drawings. I can build them with cubes.

Key words
cube, cuboid, flat, layer

Make a cuboid with one
layer of nine cubes.

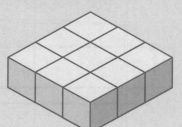

Remove three cubes to
make a flat 3-D shape.

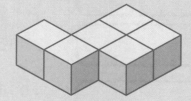

Imagine the joins of the
cubes are not there.

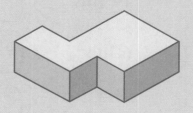

1 Get some interlocking cubes.
Work out the number of cubes you need to build these shapes.
Check by building each shape.
Write the number of cubes you used.

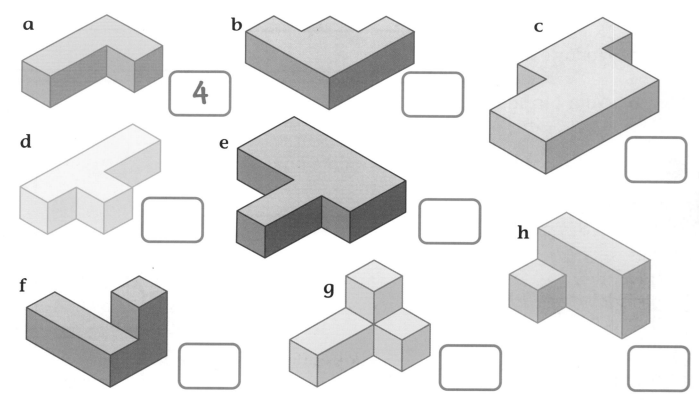

a 4

b

c

d

e

f

g

h

2 Terry's job in a supermarket is to fill the shelves and make a cuboid display of each kind of packet.
Work out the number of packets Terry needs to add to make each display a cuboid.

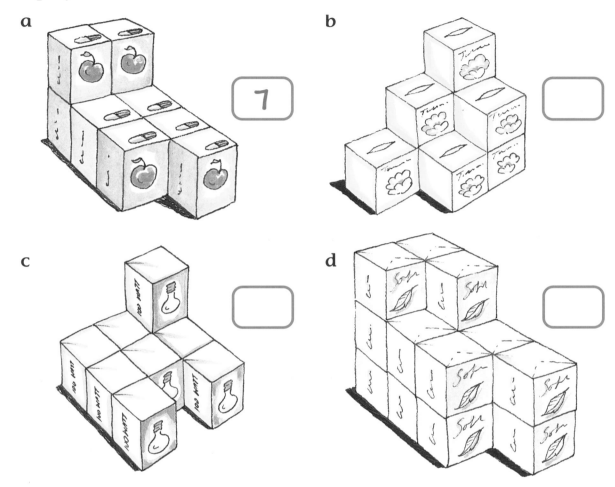

a

7

b

☐

c

☐

d

☐

◆ I can recognise solid shapes from drawings and build them with cubes. ☐

Get some interlocking cubes.
Work out the least number of cubes you will need to build a cuboid.
Check by building the cuboid.

a  b  c  d

9.2 Nets of 3-D shapes

● I can recognise 3-D shapes from their nets.

Key words
net, cube, cuboid, square-based pyramid, triangular prism

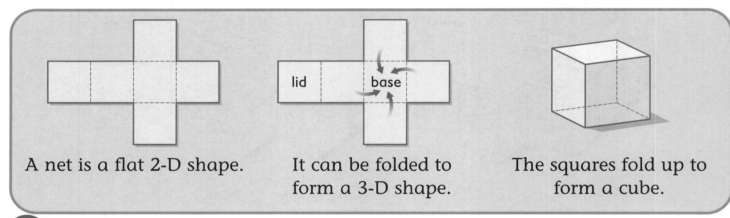

A net is a flat 2-D shape.

It can be folded to form a 3-D shape.

The squares fold up to form a cube.

1 Name the 3-D shape you can make from each net.

cube　　　cuboid　　　triangular prism　　　square-based pyramid

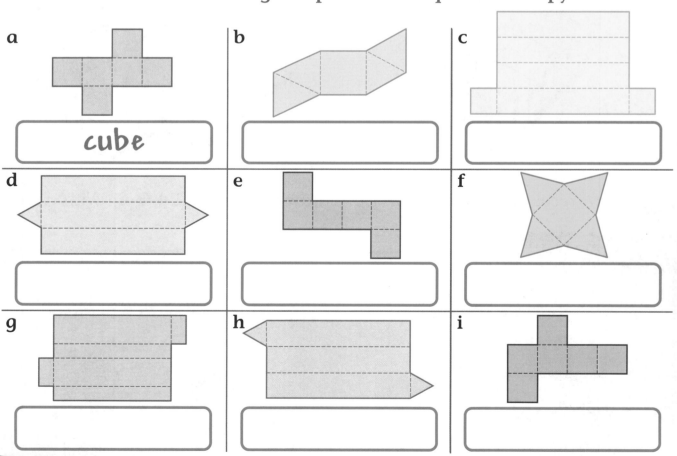

a

cube

b

c

d

e

f

g

h

i

2 Get five interlocking square tiles.
This shape will form an open cube.
Some of these shapes are nets of open cubes.
- Make each shape with five square tiles.
- Test whether or not the shape is the net of an open cube.
- If the shape is a net, write **base** on the correct square.

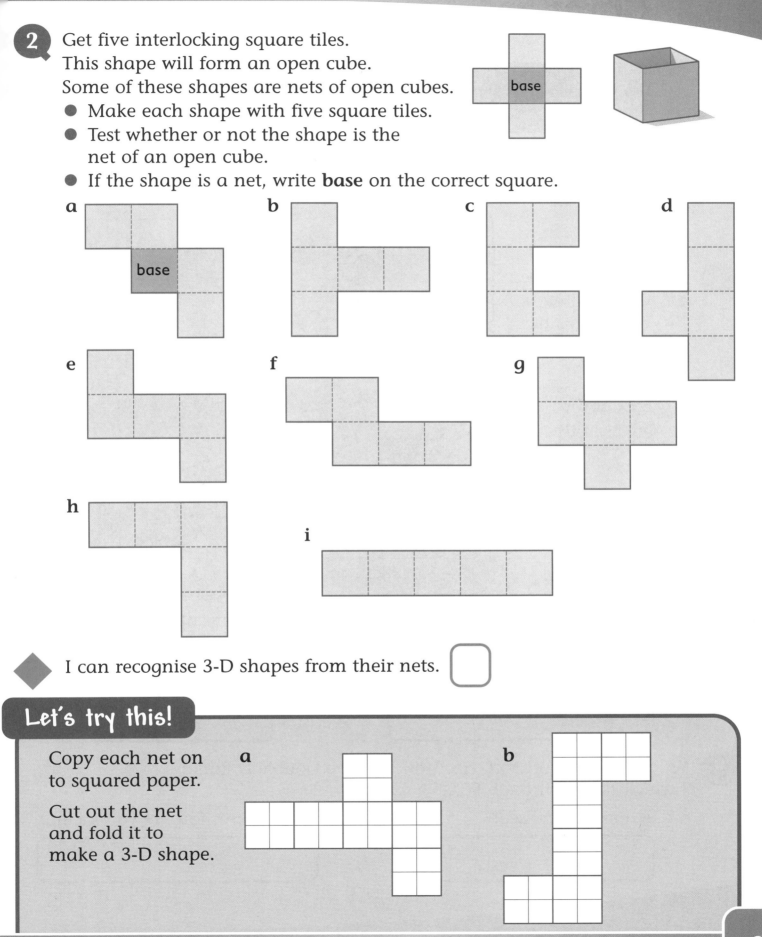

I can recognise 3-D shapes from their nets.

Let's try this!

Copy each net on to squared paper.

Cut out the net and fold it to make a 3-D shape.

a

b

Compass points

● I can use the eight compass directions.

Key words
compass, direction, north-east (NE), north-west (NW), south-east (SE), south-west (SW), clockwise, diagonally

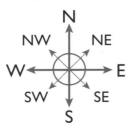

1 Write what you see:

a West of the Wagon Train.

b East of the Silver Mine.

c South of Fort McLean.

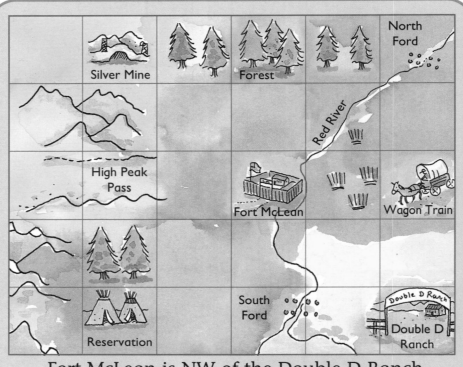

Fort McLean is NW of the Double D Ranch.

2 You are at Fort McLean. What do you see when you face these directions?

a NW

b SE

c NE

d SW

3 You are still at Fort McLean. Now face the Double D Ranch. Turn clockwise through 90°.

a What can you see?

b Which direction are you facing?

4 **a** You will need pencils in three colours.
Start at ○ and end at △.
You can move diagonally.
Follow these compass directions and colour the route you will take.
The first direction (6N) is shown.

6N, 2NW, 3SW, 2W, 3S.

b Colour two different routes from △ back to ○.

Write your directions below.

Route 1

Route 2

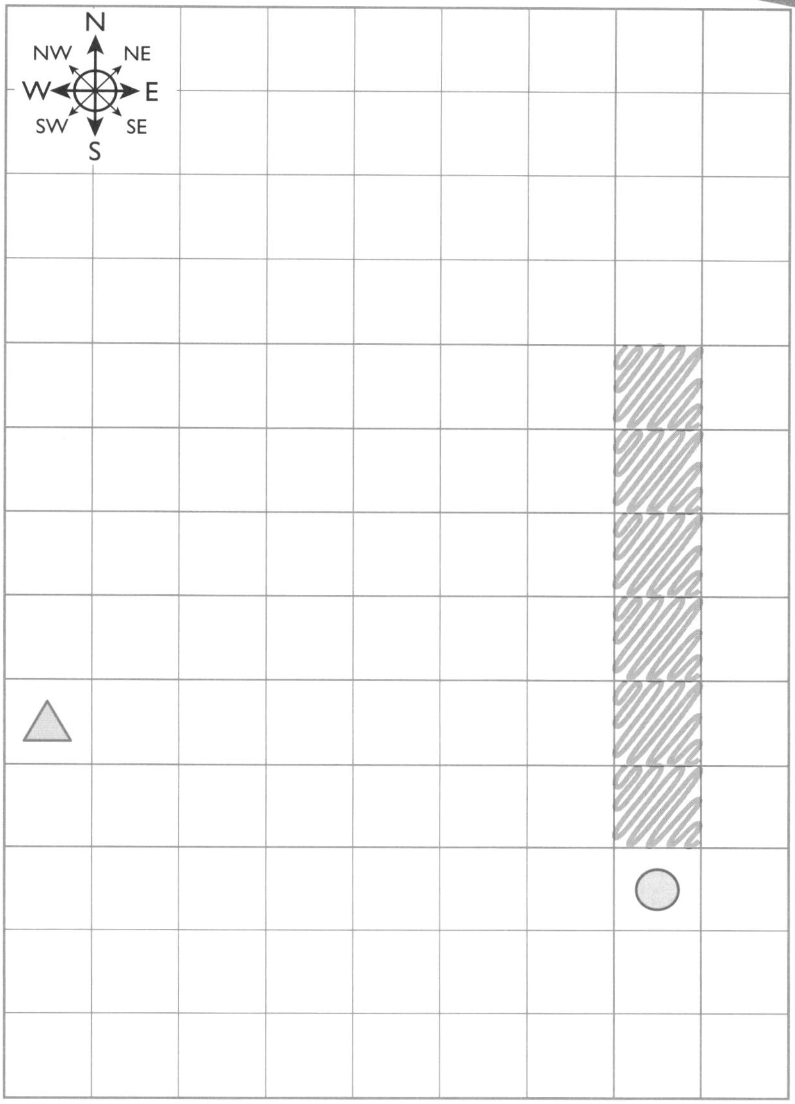

I can use the eight compass directions. ☐

Let's try this!

Look at the map on page 88.
a Write a route for the Wagon Train which crosses the Red River at a ford, stops at Fort McLean and then continues to the High Peaks Pass.

b Write a route from the Reservation to the North Ford which avoids Fort McLean.

9.4 Set square angles

- I can measure angles of 90°, 60°, 45° and 30° and order angles less than 180°.

Key words
angle, right angle, set square, degrees (°), clockwise, anticlockwise

When the wind blows, the weather vane always turns the shortest way.

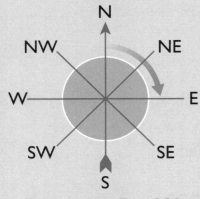

From N to E = 90°

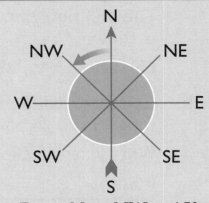

From N to NW = 45°

1 Get a 90°, 45°, 45° set square.
Write the amount of turn made by the weather vane.

a From N to NE **45°**

b From SE to S

c From W to N

d From SW to W

e From E to SW

f From SW to N

2 Write the direction the weather vane will face after these turns.

a From S clockwise 90° **W**

b From E anticlockwise 90°

c From SE clockwise 45°

d From NE anticlockwise 45°

3 The hands on a clock always turn clockwise.

Write the amount of turn made by the hour hand.

12 o'clock to 1 o'clock = 30°

12 o'clock to 2 o'clock = 60°

12 o'clock to 3 o'clock = 90°

a 1 o'clock to 2 o'clock 〔 **30°** 〕   **b** 3 o'clock to 5 o'clock 〔 〕

c 6 o'clock to 9 o'clock 〔 〕   **d** 8 o'clock to 10 o'clock 〔 〕

e 7 o'clock to 8 o'clock 〔 〕   **f** 11 o'clock to 2 o'clock 〔 〕

4 Get a 90°, 45°, 45° set square and a 90°, 60°, 30° set square.

You can measure the angles greater than a right angle by putting together the angles of two set squares.

a Use your set squares to find the size of each angle.

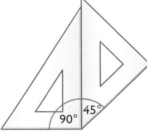

90° + 45° = 135°

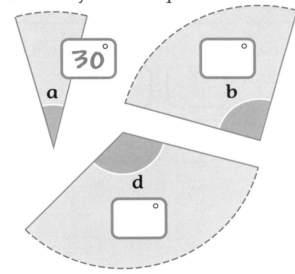

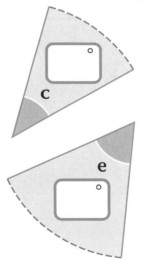

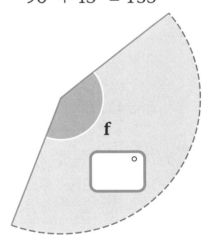

a 30° **b** 〔 ° 〕 **c** 〔 ° 〕 **d** 〔 ° 〕 **e** 〔 ° 〕 **f** 〔 ° 〕

b Order the angles beginning with the smallest. 〔 〕

◆ I can measure angles of 90°, 60°, 45° and 30° and order angles less than 180°. 〔 〕

Let's try this!

Use a ruler and a set square to draw a triangle with:
a two angles of 60°.   **b** an angle of 30° and an angle of 45°.

9.5 Using co-ordinates

● I can read and plot
co-ordinates to make shapes.

Key words
position, grid, co-ordinates,
x-axis, y-axis, direction, plot

The grid shows the position of
the Red team's players in
a five-a-side football game.

To find A's position:

Start from 0.

Go **along** on the x-axis ⟶ to **1**

then **up** on the y-axis ↑ to **2**.

A's co-ordinates are (**1**, **2**)

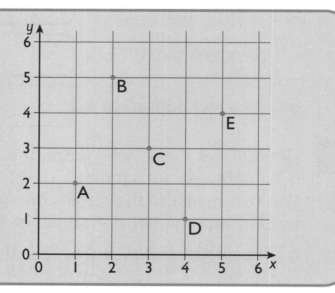

1 Look at the co-ordinate grid. Write the co-ordinates for these players.

   a B (**2** , **5**)

   b C (⬚ , ⬚)

   c D (⬚ , ⬚)

   d E (⬚ , ⬚)

2 On this grid plot the points
for the Blue team.

K (6, 3)

L (5, 1)

M (3, 6)

N (0, 2)

O (1, 4)

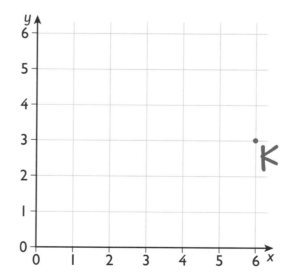

3 Get a ruler.

a Write the co-ordinates of shape A.

() ()

()

b Plot these points to make shape B in the same grid.

(3, 3) (4, 5) (5, 3)

Join the points in order.

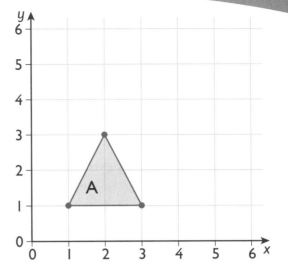

4 Get a ruler.

a Write the co-ordinates of shape C.

() ()

()

b Plot these points to make shape D in the same grid.

(3, 1) (4, 5) (5, 2)

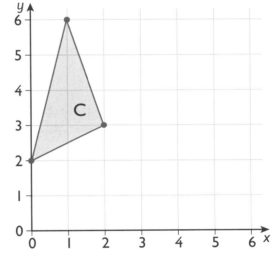

◆ I can read and plot co-ordinates to make shapes. [ ]

Let's try this!

Get a dice.

● Throw the dice twice.
● Go **along** the number of your first throw.
● Go **up** the number of your second throw.
● Circle the co-ordinates you make.
● How many throws do you need to get three circles in the same row or column?
● Write the co-ordinates of your throws.

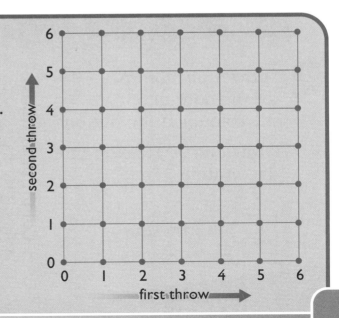

HANDLING DATA
10.1 Pictograms

● I can show data in a pictogram.

Key words
data, key, pictogram,
tally chart, frequency table

The information in this frequency
table can also be shown in a pictogram.

Colour of cars	Tally	Frequency
Red	卌 卌 卌	15
Blue	卌 卌	10

Frequency table

Key
🚗 = 5 cars

Colour of cars			
Red	🚗	🚗	🚗
Blue	🚗	🚗	

Number of cars
Pictogram

1 Count the buttons of each colour
and fill in the tally chart.

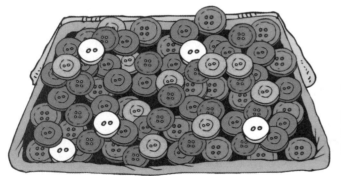

Button	Tally	Frequency
Red		
Blue		
Green		
Orange		
White		
Total		

2 Draw a pictogram
for the data about
the colours of the buttons.

Draw one ◯ to stand for
five buttons.

Key
◯ = 5 buttons

Colour of buttons						
Red						
Blue						
Green						
Orange						
White						

Number of buttons

3 The table shows the number
of rainy and sunny days for
six months.

Key

◯ = 2 rainy days

☀ = 4 sunny days

☀ = 2 sunny days

Complete the pictograms below.

Month	Rainy	Sunny
April	10	12
May	12	18
June	8	22
July	4	24
August	6	16
September	14	14

Rainy days

Months							
April	◯	◯	◯	◯	◯		
May							
June							
July							
August							
September							

Number of rainy days

Sunny days

Months							
April	☀	☀	☀				
May							
June							
July							
August							
September							

Number of sunny days

 I can show data in a pictogram. ☐

Let's try this!

In the tables, some days were sunny, some were rainy and
the remaining days were cloudy. Work out the number of cloudy days.

Draw a pictogram to show your results.

10.2 Data from experiments

• I can collect and organise data so that it is easy to understand.

Key words
record, tally chart, frequency column, data, bar chart, most / least common

The sum of two dice is 5 + 3 = 8

1 Get two dice.

a Activity
- Roll both dice.
- Add the dots on both dice.
- Record the total in the tally chart.

Do the activity 20 times.

b Complete the frequency column.

Total	Tally	Frequency
1–2		
3–4		
5–6		
7–8		
9–10		
11–12		

c Use the data in the frequency column to draw a bar chart.

d Write which totals are:

the most common.

the least common.

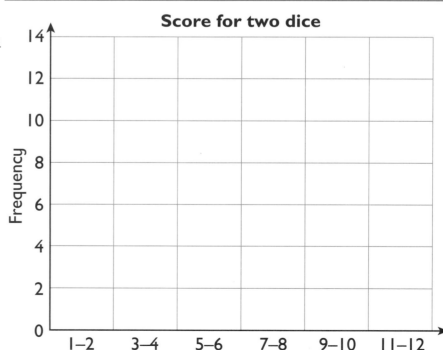

Score for two dice

The total number of dots is 10.

2 Get a set of dominoes.

a **Activity**
- Shuffle the dominoes face down on the table.
- Choose two dominoes.
- Add the dots on both dominoes.
- Record the total in the tally chart.

Do this activity 20 times.

b Complete the frequency column.

c Use the data in the frequency column to draw a bar chart.

d Write which totals are:

the most common.

the least common.

Total	Tally	Frequency
0–4		
5–9		
10–14		
15–19		
20–24		

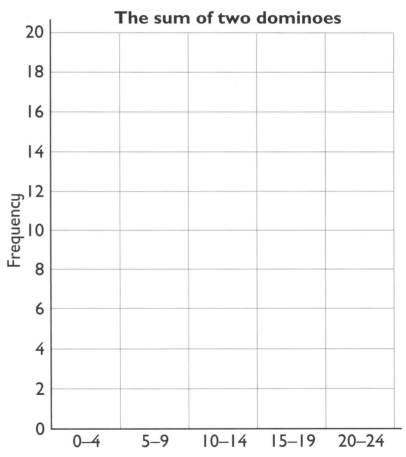

The sum of two dominoes

 I can collect and organise data so that it is easy to understand.

Let's try this!

You will need two dice and some squared paper.
Repeat the activity in question 1 on page 96,
but this time multiply the dots on both dice.
Draw a tally chart to record each roll.
Present your results in a bar chart.

$4 \times 5 = 20$

10.3 Bar charts

- I can compare bar charts with different scales.

Key words
bar chart, data, scale, horizontal axis, vertical axis

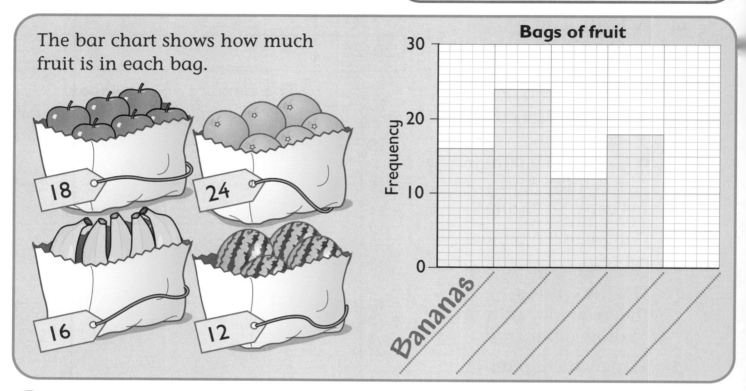

The bar chart shows how much fruit is in each bag.

18

24

16

12

1 Look at the bags of fruit and the bar chart for bags of fruit.

a Write the names of each fruit on the horizontal axis.

b How many more apples are there:

than bananas ? [ ]   than melons? [ ]

c Look at the number of pears in this bag.
Draw a column to show this data in the bar chart.

15

d The chef used 5 apples, 2 oranges, 4 bananas, 1 melon and 3 pears to make a bowl of fruit salad. How much of each fruit was left?

Apples [ ]   Oranges [ ]   Bananas [ ]

Melons [ ]   Pears [ ]

2 Students in Year 9 were asked, 'How much sleep did you have last night?'

a   How much sleep did most students have?

How many students had:

b   6 hours sleep?

c   more than 8 hours sleep?

d   less than 6 hours sleep?

e   between 7 and 8 hours sleep?

f   How many students took part?

Hours of sleep

3 a   Show the data from question 2 on this bar chart.

b   Compare the two bar charts.

In which bar chart is the data displayed more clearly?

Give a reason for your answer.

....

....

....

....

....

Hours of sleep

◆ I can compare bar charts with different scales.

Let's try this!

Draw a bar chart for the data in question 1 on page 98. Use a different scale for the vertical axis. Which chart displays the data more clearly?

Venn and Carroll diagrams

- I can organise shapes using Venn and Carroll diagrams.

Key words
overlap, Venn diagram, Carroll diagram, organise

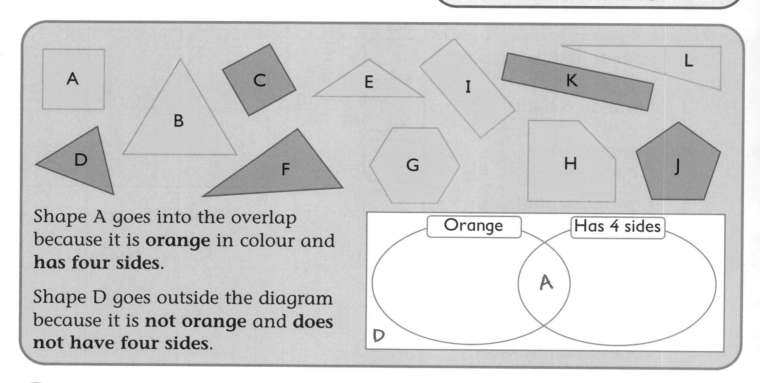

Shape A goes into the overlap because it is **orange** in colour and **has four sides**.

Shape D goes outside the diagram because it is **not orange** and **does not have four sides**.

1 Get a set square.

Write the letter of each shape above in the correct space in the Venn diagrams.

Use all the shapes for 1a and 1b.

Count the shapes. Write the totals in the boxes.

a
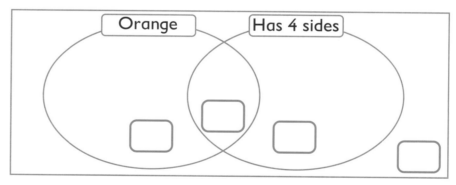

b
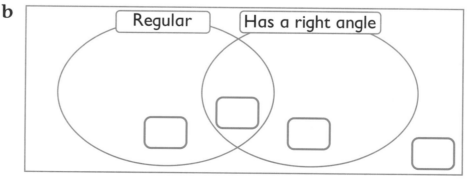

2 Look at the Venn diagram in question 1a.
How many shapes:

a are orange? `7`

b have four sides?

c are not orange and do not have four sides?

d Write the letter of each shape in the correct set in this Carroll diagram.

	Has 4 sides	Does not have 4 sides
Orange		
Not orange		

3 Look at the Venn diagram in question 1b.
How many shapes:

a are regular?

b are squares?

c do not have a right angle?

d Write the letter of each shape in the correct set in this Carroll diagram.

	Regular	Irregular
Right angle		
No right angle		

◆ I can organise shapes using Venn and Carroll diagrams.

Let's try this!

Draw a Venn diagram and a Carroll diagram.

Organise the shapes A to L on page 100 as follows:

- Has a line of symmetry
- All sides equal

10.5 Chance

● I can say how likely an event is to happen.

Key words
event, chance, even chance, certain, odd, even

The chance of an event happening can range from impossible to certain.

Event	Chance
Tomorrow you will be a day younger.	No chance
The baby will be a boy or a girl.	Even chance
The sun will rise in the morning.	Certain

1 Write the words that best describe these events – no chance, even chance, certain.

a   The day after Sunday will be Monday.   `certain`

b   I will see a dinosaur on my way home from school.

c   The first person I meet tomorrow will be male or female.

d   England will win the World Cup with a score of 50–0.

e   Next year I will be 1 metre taller.

f   A number rolled on a dice will be odd or even.

g   There are 110 pence in £1.

h   A tossed coin will land heads or tails.

2 Write three events where the chance of it happening is:

a   Certain

b   Even chance

c   No chance

3 We can put events on a scale from No chance to Certain.

| No chance | Poor chance | Even chance | Good chance | Certain |

These players have four cards each.

Andy's cards: 5 5 1 3

Ben's cards: 1 2 4 5

Amy's cards: 5 5 5 5

Lola's cards: 4 6 8 10

a Choose from:

No chance, Poor chance, Even chance, Good chance, Certain

Each player turns over their top card.

For each player write what chance he/she has that the card is a 5.

Andy [ ]   Ben [ ]   Amy [ ]   Lola [ ]

b Write who has the best chance of turning over:

an even number. [ ]   an odd number. [ ]

c Write who has the least chance of turning over:

a card greater than 5. [ ]   a card less than 4. [ ]

◆ I can say how likely an event is to happen. [ ]

Let's try this!

You will need a dice and a tally chart.

Roll the dice 20 times.

For each roll record the score as odd or even.

Total	Tally	Frequency
Odd		
Even		

Write about your results. Do it again 20 more times.

Compare both sets of scores and write what you notice.

William Collins' dream of knowledge for all began with the publication of his first book in 1819.
A self-educated mill worker, he not only enriched millions of lives, but also founded a
flourishing publishing house. Today, staying true to this spirit, Collins books are packed with
inspiration, innovation and practical expertise. They place you at the centre of a world of
possibility and give you exactly what you need to explore it.

Collins. Freedom to teach.

Published by Collins
An imprint of HarperCollins*Publishers*
77–85 Fulham Palace Road
Hammersmith
London
W6 8JB

Browse the complete Collins catalogue at
www.collinseducation.com

10 9 8 7 6 5 4 3 2 1

ISBN-13 978-0-00-730287-1

Jeanette Mumford, Simon and Helen Greaves assert their moral rights to be
identified as the authors of this work

British Library Cataloguing in Publication Data
A Catalogue record for this publication is available from the British Library.

Commissioned by Priya Govindan
Literacy review by Cliff Moon
Proofread by Lynn Watkins
Design and typesetting by Mark Walker and Steve Evans Design
Covers by Julie Martin
Illustrations by Mark Walker
Production by Therese Theron
Printed and bound by Martins the Printers, Berwick-upon-Tweed

Mixed Sources
Product group from well-managed
forests and other controlled sources
www.fsc.org   Cert no. SW-COC-1806
© 1996 Forest Stewardship Council

FSC is a non-profit international organisation established to promote the
responsible management of the world's forests. Products carrying the FSC
label are independently certified to assure consumers that they come
from forests that are managed to meet the social, economic and
ecological needs of present and future generations.

Find out more about HarperCollins and the environment at
www.harpercollins.co.uk/green

Answers

CHAPTER 1 NUMBER AND ALGEBRA

1.1 Place value in numbers
1 **b** 287 **c** 418 **d** 1581 **e** 3400
f 306 **g** 940 **h** 2809
2 **b** six hundred and twenty-five
c eight hundred and eighty-two
d one thousand, nine hundred and seventy-four
e six hundred and seventy
f two thousand, two hundred and nineteen
g four hundred and eight
h three thousand, nine hundred and twenty
3 **b** 1 thousand **c** 1 unit **d** 8 hundreds

Let's try this!
Various answers, for example, roll 4, 5, 6 and 8 to make 4568 and write as four thousand, five hundred and sixty-eight.

1.2 Ordering numbers
1 **b** 896 **c** 585 **d** 290 **e** 1800
f 1790 **g** 3475 **h** 2388
2 **b** 314 **c** 531 **d** 1219 **e** 1920 **f** 1864
3 **b** 538, 624, 752, 908
c 399, 462, 491, 506
d 1612, 1634, 2620, 4601
e 1668, 1818, 1888, 1961

Let's try this!
Various, for example, 2579, 5927, 7295, 9725.

1.3 Rounding numbers to the nearest 10 and 100
1 **b** 50 **c** 80 **d** 50
2 **b** 30 **c** 40 **d** 80
3 **a** 400 **b** 600 **c** 600 **d** 500
4 **a** 300 **b** 200 **c** 800 **d** 400

Let's try this!
Various, for example, 346 rounds to 300.

1.4 Negative numbers
1 **b** −6, −4, −2, 1, 4 **c** −8, −6, −4, −3, 2
d −4, −3, −2, −1, 1, 3, 4
2 **b** −1 **c** −5 **d** −4 **e** −10
f −5 **g** −12 **h** −8 **i** −21
3 **a** −2, −1, 0 **b** 0, −1, −2 **c** −6, −5, −4
d −5, −6, −7 **e** −12, −11, −10 **f** −11, −12, −13

Let's try this!
Various, for example, choose −4 and roll 3, so count back from 3, 2, 1, 0, −1, −2, −3, −4.

1.5 Sequences
1 **b** −40, −30, −20, −10 **c** −10, −5, 0, 5
d 1, −1, −3, −5 **e** −10, −20, −30, −40
f −10, −15, −20, −25
2 Reading down: add 10, add 5, subtract 5, subtract 10, add 2.
3 **a** −4, 8, 12 **b** −30, −20, −15, 0
c −9, −6, 0, 6 **d** 5, 0, −5, −20
e 4, 0, −8, −16

Let's try this!
Various, for example, choose subtract 3 and 0 to give the sequence 0, −3, −6, −9, −12, −15.

CHAPTER 2 FRACTIONS AND DECIMALS

2.1 Fraction of a shape
1 **b** Shade any three squares
c Shade any seven squares
d Shade any five triangles
e Shade any three squares
f Shade any four rectangles
2 **b** $\frac{5}{6}$ **c** $\frac{8}{10}$ **d** $\frac{5}{8}$
3 **a** $\frac{3}{6}$ **b** $\frac{5}{8}$ **c** $\frac{5}{8}$
d $\frac{4}{6}$ **e** $\frac{4}{10}$ **f** $\frac{3}{8}$
4 **a** $\frac{3}{6}$ left, $\frac{3}{6}$ eaten **b** $\frac{3}{8}$ left, $\frac{5}{8}$ eaten
c $\frac{7}{9}$ left, $\frac{2}{9}$ eaten

Let's try this!
$\frac{2}{4}, \frac{2}{6}, \frac{2}{7}, \frac{2}{8}, \frac{2}{9}, \frac{4}{6}, \frac{4}{7}, \frac{4}{8}, \frac{4}{9}, \frac{6}{7}, \frac{6}{8}, \frac{6}{9}, \frac{7}{8}, \frac{7}{9}, \frac{8}{9}$

2.2 Equivalent fractions
1 Tick a, c, e, h
2 **b**
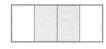
c   **d**
3 **b** $\frac{5}{10} = \frac{1}{2}$ **c** $\frac{3}{6} = \frac{1}{2}$ **d** $\frac{2}{8} = \frac{1}{4}$

Let's try this!
For $\frac{1}{2}$ check that four squares have been shaded in four different ways.

For $\frac{1}{4}$ check that two squares have been shaded in four different ways.

2.3 Fraction of a number

1 a 4, 6   **b** 4, 8, 12

2 a 8   **b** 6, 12   **c** 7, 21

   d 5, 15   **e** 7, 14   **f** 5, 15

Let's try this!

Various, for example, $\frac{1}{2}$ of 12 = 6, $\frac{2}{3}$ of 12 = 8.

2.4 Mixed numbers

1 b $2\frac{1}{2}$ **c** $1\frac{1}{4}$ **d** $2\frac{3}{4}$

   e $1\frac{1}{3}$ **f** $1\frac{4}{5}$ **g** $2\frac{1}{6}$

2 b Shade nine rectangles in total

   c Shade four rectangles in total

   d Shade seven rectangles in total

   e Shade eleven rectangles in total

   f Shade thirteen rectangles in total

Let's try this!

For example, for $1\frac{3}{4}$ draw two squares divided into four equal parts and shade one complete square and three parts of the other square.

2.5 Tenths as decimals

1 b Shade three squares   **c** Shade eight squares

   d Shade two squares

2 b 0.4   **c** 0.9   **d** 0.5

3 b 1.5   **c** 1.8   **d** 2.3

Let's try this!

For example, for $1\frac{2}{10}$, write 1.2. Draw two strips of 10 squares. Shade one complete strip and 2 squares of the other strip.

$2\frac{7}{10} = 2.7$, $5\frac{1}{10} = 5.1$, $\frac{3}{10} = 0.3$, $\frac{9}{10} = 0.9$, $10\frac{5}{10} = 10.5$

Chapter 3
Addition And Subtraction

3.1 Adding two two-digit numbers

1 b 71   **c** 101   **d** 110   **e** 94

   f 82   **g** 125   **h** 121

2 b 92   **c** 133   **d** 181

Let's try this!

For example, choose 37 and 46 to make 37 + 46 = 83.

3.2 Adding a two-digit number to a three-digit number

1 b 261   **c** 206   **d** 311   **e** 193

   f 352   **g** 206   **h** 321

2 b 331   **c** 430   **d** 605

Let's try this!

Various answers with the following giving totals of more than 300:

38 + 263 = 301, 49 + 263 = 312.

3.3 Adding two three-digit numbers

1 b 382   **c** 311   **d** 402   **e** 576

   f 599   **g** 708   **h** 553

2 a 267   **b** 298   **c** 399   **d** 399

Let's try this!

Various answers with the following giving totals of less than 500:

101 + 268 = 369, 101 + 245 = 346, 101 + 341 = 442.

3.4 Subtracting two two-digit numbers

1 b 43   **c** 14   **d** 48   **e** 29   **f** 56

2 b 41   **c** 29   **d** 19   **e** 44

   f 34   **g** 37   **h** 18

Let's try this!

For example 84 − 52 = 32.
The largest difference is given by 90 − 17 = 73 and the smallest difference is given by 68 − 63 = 5.

3.5 Subtracting a two-digit number from a three-digit number

1 b 75   **c** 86   **d** 65   **e** 156   **f** 172

2 b 59   **c** 131   **d** 194   **e** 133

   f 172   **g** 263   **h** 289

Let's try this!

For example, 185 − 52 = 133 or 341 − 79 = 262.

Chapter 4
Multiplication And Division

4.1 Six and eight times tables

1 c 3, 18   **d** 4, 24   **e** 5, 30   **f** 6, 36

   g 7, 42   **h** 8, 48   **i** 9, 54   **j** 10, 60

2 b 32   **c** 30   **d** 7   **e** 6

   f 10   **g** 9   **h** 3   **i** 4

3 a 42, 48   **b** 64, 72, 48

   c 3, 5, 2   **d** 3, 1, 2

Let's try this!

For example, 1 × 4 = 4 and 1 × 8 = 8 and 8 is double 4, or 2 × 4 = 8, 2 × 8 = 16 and 16 is double 8.

4.2 Seven and nine times tables

1 a 45, 90, 18   **b** 27, 63, 72, 54   **c** 3, 6, 5, 9

2 a 35, 7, 70   **b** 21, 28, 63, 49   **c** 4, 9, 7, 11

3 21, 28, 35, 42, 7, 70, 14, 49, 56, 63

4 9, 36, 90, 18, 72, 54, 45, 27, 81, 63

Let's try this!

For example, choose 36: 6 × 6 = 36 and 4 × 9 = 36.

4.3 Multiplying and dividing by 10

1 b 630   **c** 980   **d** 1600   **e** 1760   **f** 2900

2 b 23   **c** 300   **d** 179   **e** 360   **f** 905

3 b ÷   **c** ×   **d** ÷   **e** ×
f ÷   **g** ÷   **h** ×

Let's try this!
Various answers possible.

4.4 Multiplying a two-digit number by a one-digit number

1 b 450   **c** 240   **d** 360
2 b 210   **c** 152   **d** 246   **e** 270   **f** 207
3 b 94   **c** 380   **d** 216

Let's try this!
For example, choose 28 and × 4 to give 112,
or 68 and × 3 to give 204.

4.5 Dividing with remainders

1 b 4   **c** 10   **d** 5   **e** 7
f 9   **g** 9   **h** 8   **i** 7
2 a $20 \div 5 = 4$ so $24 \div 5 = 4$ r 4
    $35 \div 5 = 7$ so $36 \div 5 = 7$ r 1
    $45 \div 5 = 9$ so $47 \div 5 = 9$ r 2
b $15 \div 3 = 5$ so $16 \div 3 = 5$ r 1
    $6 \div 3 = 2$ so $7 \div 3 = 2$ r 1
    $30 \div 3 = 10$ so $32 \div 3 = 10$ r 2
c $8 \div 4 = 2$ so $9 \div 4 = 2$ r 1
    $28 \div 4 = 7$ so $30 \div 4 = 7$ r 2
    $20 \div 4 = 5$ so $22 \div 4 = 5$ r 2
3 b $50 \div 5 = 10$, $30 \div 5 = 6$, $20 \div 5 = 4$
c $32 \div 4 = 8$, $16 \div 4 = 4$, $8 \div 4 = 2$
d $19 \div 2 = 9$ r 1, $13 \div 2 = 6$ r 1, $7 \div 2 = 3$ r 1
e $36 \div 5 = 7$ r 1, $24 \div 5 = 4$ r 4

Let's try this!
For example, choose 24 and ÷ 5 to give 4 r 4.

CHAPTER 5 MONEY

5.1 Pounds and pence

1 b 5, 500   **c** 7, 700   **d** 8, 800
e 10, 1000   **f** 12, 1200
2 b £7 = £2 + £2 + £2 + £1
c £4 = £2 + £2
d £10 = £2 + £2 + £2 + £2 + £2
e £13 = £2 + £2 + £2 + £2 + £2 + £2 + £1
3 b £18   **c** £22   **d** £1   **e** £19

Let's try this!
9 £1 coins, 7 £1 coins and 1 £2 coin, 5 £1 coins and 2 £2 coins,
3 £1 coins and 3 £2 coins, 1 £1 coin and 4 £2 coins.

5.2 Making pounds using other coins

1 b 50   **c** 20   **d** 10   **e** 5   **f** 2
2 Tick a, d, e, f, g

3 b 20p   20p
c 50p
d 10p   10p   10p
e 5p   5p
f 2p   2p   1p

Let's try this!
There are many possible answers, for example,
50p + 50p (2 coins),
50p + 20p + 20p + 10p (4 coins),
20p + 20p + 20p + 20p + 10p + 10p (6 coins).

5.3 Pounds and pence decimal notation

1 b 125p = £1.25   **c** 131p = £1.31
d 157p = £1.57   **e** 223p = £2.23
f 405p = £4.05   **g** 257p = £2.57
h 553p = £5.53
2 b 504p   **c** 850p   **d** 64p   **e** 8p
3 b £0.95   **c** £2.30   **d** £0.06   **e** £4.03
4 a £3.52   **b** 190p   **c** £2.90

Let's try this!
For example, choose one £1 coin, one 50p coin and
four 10p coins to make 190p or £1.90.

5.4 Addition problems with money

1 b £1.40   **c** £1.10   **d** £1.31
e £1.84   **f** £1.66
2 b £4.30   **c** £6.75   **d** £2.66
e £4.62   **f** £3.23
3 a £2.20   **b** £3.10   **c** £2.40

Let's try this!
For example, choose £3.67 and £1.35 and work out
the total as £5.02.

5.5 Subtraction problems with money

1 b £1.25   **c** £4.25   **d** £9.25
2 b £2.70   **c** 34p   **d** £3.71
3 b £1.82   **c** £1.18   **d** £2.41

Let's try this!
For example, choose £2.60 and £2.17 and work out
the total as £4.77. The change from £5 will be 23p.

CHAPTER 6
MEASURE – LENGTH AND TIME

6.1 Measuring in millimetres
[Note: Allow differences of ± 1 mm in answers]
1 b 40 mm   **c** 68 mm   **d** 48 mm   **e** 22 mm
f 35 mm   **g** 78 mm   **h** 42 mm
2 a AB = 45 mm   **b** AC = 64 mm
3 a AB = 27 mm = 2 cm 7 mm
b BD = 47 mm = 4 cm 7 mm

Let's try this!

a B 92 mm = 9.2 cm   C 103 mm = 10.3 cm
   D 119 mm = 11.9 cm   E 124 mm = 12.4 cm
   F 136 mm = 13.6 cm

b Distance from A to E = 3.9 cm

6.2 Using metric units of length

1

Kilometres	1 km	$\frac{1}{2}$ km	$\frac{1}{4}$ km	$\frac{1}{10}$ km	$\frac{3}{4}$ km
Metres	1000 m	500 m	250 m	100 m	750 m

2 a 1250 m   **b** 4750 m   **c** 2100 m
   d 750 m   **e** $4\frac{1}{10}$ km   **f** $\frac{1}{4}$ km

3 a

Metres	1 m	$\frac{1}{2}$ m	$\frac{1}{4}$ m	$\frac{1}{10}$ m	$\frac{3}{4}$ m
Centimetres	100 cm	50 cm	25 cm	10 cm	75 cm

b

Metres	0.2 m	0.5 m	0.7 m	0.4 m	0.9 m	0.8 m	0.6 m
Centimetres	20 cm	50 cm	70 cm	40 cm	90 cm	80 cm	60 cm

4 a 1900 m   **b** 2200 m   **c** 1750 m
   d 2100 m   **e** 1800 m   **f** 1700 m
   g 1700 m, 1750 m, 1800 m, 1900 m, 2100 m, 2200 m

Let's try this!
Each lamp post is 200 m apart.

6.3 Perimeter
1 b 14 cm   **c** 16 cm   **d** 18 cm   **e** 18 cm
2 Check that the rectangles are complete.

Rectangle	a	b	c	d	e	f	g
Perimeter	12 cm	16 cm	12 cm	14 cm	10 cm	18 cm	10 cm

Let's try this!
a 12 cm   **b** 12 cm   **c** 12 cm

6.4 Area
1 b 8 square cm   **c** 9 square cm
   d 15 square cm   **e** 12 square cm
   f 16 square cm
2 a 8 square cm   **b** 6 square cm
   c 6 square cm   **d** 11 square cm
   e 9 square cm
3 a   **b**   **c**

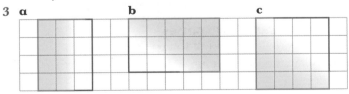

Let's try this!
Area of E = 25 square cm   Perimeter of E = 20 cm

6.5 Time to the minute
1 b 7 min past 4 4:07   **c** 19 min past 9 9:19
   d 25 min to 8 7:35   **e** 13 min to 4 3:47
   f 4 min to 5 4:56   **g** 9 min past 10 10:09
   h 17 min to 12 11:43
2 b 4:58   58 minutes past 4   2 minutes to 5
   c 7:46   46 minutes past 7   14 minutes to 8
   d 9:51   51 minutes past 9   9 minutes to 10
   e 10:47   47 minutes past 10   13 minutes to 11
3 a 7 min past 2   **b** 26 min past 8
   c 12 min past 4   **d** 16 min to 12
   e 24 min to 5   **f** 8 min to 1

Let's try this!
a 8:58   **b** 12:03   **c** 9:23   **d** 8:33

CHAPTER 7
UNDERSTANDING SHAPES

7.1 More or less than a right angle
1

Less than a right angle	b, c, d, g
More than a right angle	a, e, f

2 acute angles: b, c, e, g
   obtuse angles: a, d, f
3 b right   **c** acute   **d** obtuse

Let's try this!
a and d

7.2 Equilateral and right-angled triangles
1 a Check the triangles are complete.
   b right-angled   **c** other   **d** other
   e equilateral   **f** right-angled

2

Equilateral	Right-angled	Other
a, e	b, f	c, d

3

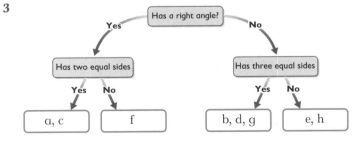

Let's try this!
Help students with practical activity if appropriate.

7.3 Horizontal or vertical?
1 b vertical   **c** horizontal   **d** vertical
   e horizontal   **f** horizontal   **g** vertical
   h horizontal   **i** vertical

2 a H **b** V **c** S
d S **e** H **f** H

3

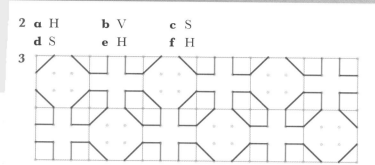

Let's try this!
Six capital letters are: E, F, H, I, L, and T.

7.4 Regular or irregular shapes?

1 a

Regular	Irregular
a, c, f, h, j	b, d, e, g, i, j, l

b

Has a right angle	Has no right angle
b, c, d, k, l	a, e, f, g, h, i, j

2 a

	Regular	Irregular
Has three sides	h	b
Has four sides	c	e, g, k, l

b

	Regular	Irregular
Line symmetry	a, c, f, h, j	b, d, e, g, k
No line symmetry		i, l

3

Property	2-D shape
Has all sides equal	a, c, f, g, h, j
Has two or more right angles	c, d, k
Has two or more lines of symmetry	a, c, f, g, h, j, k

Let's try this!

Property	2-D shape
Has all sides equal	b
Has one or more obtuse angles	a, c, d, e, g, h
Has one or more lines of symmetry	b, d, e, f, g

7.5 Symmetry patterns and puzzles

1 a 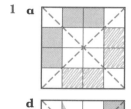 **b** 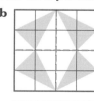 **c**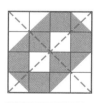

d 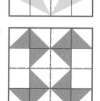 **e** **f**

2 a

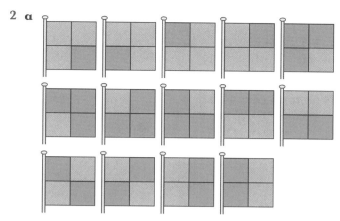

b 1 line of symmetry: 12   2 lines of symmetry: 2

Let's try this!

Regular shape	a	b	c	d	e
Number of sides	4	5	6	7	8
Number of lines of symmetry	4	5	6	7	8

CHAPTER 8
MEASURE –
WEIGHT, CAPACITY AND TIME

8.1 Grams and kilograms
1 b $3\frac{1}{4}$ kg = 3250 g   **c** $6\frac{3}{4}$ kg = 6750 g
d $9\frac{1}{4}$ kg = 9250 g   **e** $7\frac{1}{2}$ kg = 7500 g
f $1\frac{6}{10}$ kg = 1600 g   **g** $1\frac{3}{10}$ kg = 1300 g
h $\frac{9}{10}$ kg = 900 g
2 b 200 g + 50 g   **c** 100 g + 50 g
d 200 g + 100 g + 50 g   **e** 500 g + 200 g + 100 g
3 b 7100 g   **c** 7500 g   **d** 6250 g
e 8100 g   **f** 6750 g

Let's try this!
50 g + 100 g = 150 g   100 g + 200 g = 300 g
200 g + 500 g = 700 g   50 g + 200 g = 250 g
100 g + 500 g = 600 g   50 g + 500 g = 550 g

8.2 Half and double quantities
1 b 500 g / 2000 g   **c** 300 g / 1200 g
d 200 g / 800 g   **e** 250 g / 1000 g
f 300 g / 1200 g

2

Recipe for two pies	Recipe for four pies
1000 g apples	2000 g apples
600 g blueberries	1200 g blueberries
200 g sugar	400 g sugar
100 g butter	200 g butter
500 g flour	1000 g flour

3 a 5.6 kg **b** 1200 g **c** 800 g

Let's try this!
  a 200 g **b** 100 g **c** 200 g
  d 600 g **e** 10 kg **f** 2 kg

8.3 Fractions of a litre

1 b $\frac{1}{2}$ l = 250 ml + 250 ml = 500 ml
  c $\frac{3}{4}$ l = 500 ml + 250 ml = 750 ml
  d 1 l = 250 ml + 750 ml = 1000 ml
  e $\frac{2}{10}$ l = 100 ml + 100 ml = 200 ml
  f $\frac{8}{10}$ l = 500 ml + 300 ml = 800 ml
  g $\frac{6}{10}$ l = 100 ml + 500 ml = 600 ml
  h $\frac{3}{4}$ l = 250 ml + 250 ml + 250 ml = 750 ml

2

l	0.1 l	0.2 l	0.3 l	0.5 l	0.6 l	0.8 l	0.9 l	1 l
ml	100 ml	200 ml	300 ml	500 ml	600 ml	800 ml	900 ml	1000ml

3 b 2 l 500 ml = 2500 ml **c** 4 l 200 ml = 4200 ml
  d 3 l 100 ml = 3100 ml **e** 2 l 800 ml = 2800 ml
  f 5 l 300 ml = 5300 ml **g** 2 l 700 ml = 2700 ml
  h 3 l 900 ml = 3900 ml **i** 6 l 600 ml = 6600 ml

Let's try this!
  a 1000 ml **b** 4 mugs **c** 5 glasses

8.4 Capacity problems

1 b 400 ml – 250 ml = 150 ml
  c 450 ml – 200 ml = 250 ml
  d 800 ml – 300 ml = 500 ml
2 b 2250 ml **c** 3500 ml **d** 2900 ml
  e 4400 ml **f** 3800 ml
3 a 10 times **b** 8 times **c** 6 times

Let's try this!
  a after trip A – 8 l; after trip B – 5 l; after trip C – 2.5 l
  b trip A – 2 l; trip B – 3 l; trip C – 2.5 l

8.5 Timetables and calendars

1

Central Station	10:15	10:40	11:05
Westerton	10:25	10:50	11:15
Eastfield	10:35	11:00	11:25
Southam	10:45	11:10	11:35
Norby	10:55	11:20	11:45

2 a 40 min **b** 20 min **c** 5 min
3 a 5 Thursdays, 4 Saturdays, 5 Wednesdays
  b 14 July: Tuesday   6 July: Monday
    25 July: Saturday
    The first day in July: Wednesday
    The last day in July: Friday
4 Answers will vary.

Let's try this!

Danny	6 July	Mary	29 July
Harry	9 July	Sandy	22 July

CHAPTER 9 MORE ON SHAPES

9.1 Picture 3-D shapes

1 b 6 **c** 11 **d** 5 **e** 10
  f 5 **g** 5 **h** 7
2 b 9 **c** 9 **d** 7

Let's try this!
  a 4 **b** 5 **c** 22 **d** 22

9.2 Nets of 3-D shapes

1 b square-based pyramid **c** cuboid
  d triangular prism **e** cube
  f square-based pyramid **g** cuboid
  h triangular prism **i** cube
2 The nets for an open cube are: b, d, e, f and g.

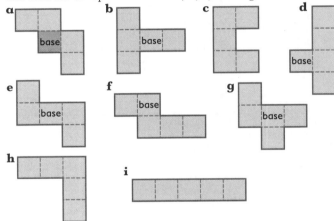

Let's try this!
Shapes a and b are cubes.

9.3 Compass points

1 a Fort McLean **b** Forest **c** South Ford
2 a Silver Mine **b** Double D Ranch
  c North Ford **d** Reservation
3 a Reservation **b** SW
4 a

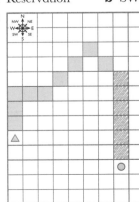

b Answers will vary.

Let's try this!
Answers will vary.

9.4 Set square angles
1 **b** 45°   **c** 90°   **d** 45°   **e** 135°   **f** 135°
2 **b** N   **c** S   **d** N
3 **b** 60°   **c** 90°   **d** 60°   **e** 30°   **f** 90°
4 **b** 90°   **c** 45°   **d** 120°   **e** 60°   **f** 150°
  b 30°, 45°, 60°, 90°, 120°, 150°

Let's try this!
Check triangles are accurate.

9.5 Using co-ordinates
1 C (3, 3), D (4, 1), E (5, 4)

2
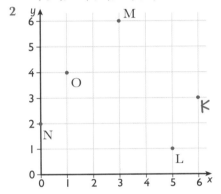

3 **a** Shape A (1, 1) (2, 3) (3, 1)
  b
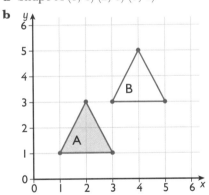

4 **a** Shape C (0, 2) (1, 6) (2, 3)
  b
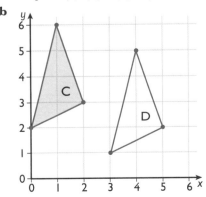

Let's try this!
Answers will vary.

CHAPTER 10 HANDLING DATA

10.1 Pictograms

1

Button	Tally	Frequency
Red	𝍏𝍏𝍏	15
Blue	𝍏𝍏𝍏𝍏	20
Green	𝍏𝍏𝍏𝍏𝍏	25
Orange	𝍏𝍏	10
White	𝍏	5
Total		**75**

2

Colour of buttons					
Red	◯	◯	◯		
Blue	◯	◯	◯	◯	
Green	◯	◯	◯	◯	◯
Orange	◯	◯			
White	◯				

Number of buttons

3

Rainy days

Months							
April	💧	💧	💧	💧	💧		
May	💧	💧	💧	💧	💧		
June	💧	💧	💧	💧			
July	💧	💧					
August	💧	💧	💧				
September	💧	💧	💧	💧	💧	💧	💧

Number of rainy days

Sunny days

Months						
April	☀	☀	☀			
May	☀	☀	☀	☀	☀	
June	☀	☀	☀	☀	☀	
July	☀	☀	☀	☀		
August	☀	☀	☀	☀		
September	☀	☀	☀			

Number of sunny days

Let's try this!
You need to know how many days are in each month.
Cloudy days: Apr: 8, May: 1, June: 0, July: 3, Aug: 9, Sept: 2.
Suggest the key is ☁ = 2 days.

10.2 Data from experiments
1 Answers will vary.
2 Answers will vary.

Let's try this!
Answers will vary.

10.3 Bar charts

1 **a** bananas, oranges, melons, apples

b 2, 6

c Check the bar chart shows 15.

d 13 apples, 22 oranges, 12 bananas, 11 melons, 12 pears

2 **a** 8 hours   **b** 15   **c** 10

d 15   **e** 40   **f** 80

3 **a**

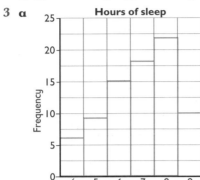

b The graph in question 2 is clearer as all intermediate intervals are shown on the vertical axis.

Let's try this!

Answers will vary.

10.4 Venn and Carroll diagrams

1 **a**

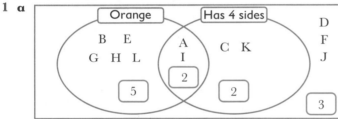

b

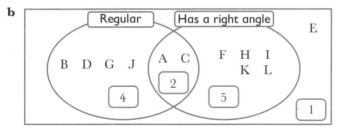

2 **b** 4   **c** 3

d

	Has 4 sides	Does not have 4 sides
Orange	A, I	B, E, G, H, L
Not orange	C, K	D, F, J

3 **a** 6   **b** 2   **c** 5

d

	Regular	Irregular
Right angle	A, C	F, H, I, K, L
No right angle	B, D, G, J	E

Let's try this!

	All sides equal	No sides equal
Line of symmetry	A, B, C, D, G, J	E, H, I, K
No line of symmetry		F, L

10.5 Chance

1 **b** no chance   **c** even chance   **d** no chance

e no chance   **f** even chance   **g** no chance

h even chance

2 Answers will vary.

3 **a** Andy: even chance   Ben: poor chance

Amy: certain   Lola: no chance

b an even number: Lola

an odd number: Andy and Amy

c a card greater than 5: Ben

a card less than 4: Amy or Lola

Let's try this!

Answers will vary but the probability that the roll of a 1–6 dice is odd or even is equally likely.